1982

# Stress
# and the
# Helping Professions

# Stress
# and the
# Helping Professions

by
**Sheldon F. Greenberg, Ph.D.**
Director, Administrative Services Bureau
Howard County Police Department
Ellicott City, Maryland

and
**Peter J. Valletutti, Ed.D.**
Professor of Special Education
Coppin State College
Baltimore, Maryland

·P·A·U·L·H·
BROOKES
PUBLISHERS

Baltimore • London

**Paul H. Brookes, Publishers**
Post Office Box 10624
Baltimore, Maryland 21204


Copyright 1980 by Paul H. Brookes Publishing Co., Inc.
All rights reserved.


Typeset by Action Comp Co., Baltimore, Maryland
Manufactured in the United States of America by Universal
    Lithographers, Inc., Cockeysville, Maryland


**Library of Congress Cataloging in Publication Data**

Greenberg, Sheldon F      1948–
    Stress and the helping professions.

    Bibliography:  p. 135
    Includes index.
    1.  Stress (Psychology)     2.  Helping behavior.
3.  Professions—Psychological aspects.     I.   Valletutti,
Peter J., joint author.     II.   Title.
BF575.S75G67      158.7      80-20328
ISBN 0-933716-09-5 (pbk.)

# Contents

v

# Preface

People who have dedicated themselves to providing services to those in need are prime candidates for the negative effects of job-related stress. They experience physical, mental, and emotional strain and tension on a daily basis. They succumb to stress-related illnesses such as headache, backache, indigestion, hypertension, fatigue, insomnia, diabetes, and more.

This text focuses on the nature of stress as it applies to human service professionals. These people often place their own well-being second to that of the clients, patients, students, and other members of the public that they serve. They work long, irregular hours, often under adverse conditions, to care for others.

Social workers, police officers, physicians, nurses, teachers, attorneys, dentists, probation and parole officers, and others are facing increased demands for their services, declining budgets, and intensified government scrutiny. Yet, they continue to provide for others in the most effective, efficient way possible. Such endeavor takes its toll on their physical and mental health, their attitude toward their work, and their relationship with their families and friends.

This text details the characteristics of the human service fields that increase the individual worker's vulnerability to the negative effects of stress. It outlines, in nontechnical language, the way in which stress affects the individual. It attempts to provide human service practitioners with a practical understanding of the stress caused by interaction with others, exposure to human grief, adherance to often ambiguous policies, and budgetary constraints.

There are many stress-causing situations in the human service fields that do not exist in other professions. Seeking funding support in order to continue functioning, facing salary increments that are not based on merit, being associated with the sometimes negative image of a "government worker," and working in a crowded environment are among the many unique stress-causing situations faced by human service workers.

In addition to presenting the causes and nature of stress, this text provides guidelines for coping with and reducing stress. Techniques are presented that can be implemented by almost all people, such as becoming diet conscious, getting involved in a new hobby or leisure activity, and exercising regularly. The text also provides programs that can be implemented by an agency or organization to assist staff members and employees in coping with and reducing the negative effects of job-related stress. Such programs range from preretirement counseling to family orientation programs. They are easy to implement, taking advantage of existing resources within the community, and generally cost little.

The human service professional who understands the causes of stress, its relationship to physical and mental illness, and the techniques for reducing it will often find that his or her attitude toward work improves significantly. By applying a few simple stress reduction techniques, job burnout and many of the physical ailments associated with a stressful work environment may be avoided.

Stress is responsible for some negative and alarming statistics in many of the human service professions. Fields such as social work, teaching, and dentistry have extremely high turnover rates in which people who have spent years preparing for their chosen fields flee to new and different occupations. In law enforcement, three times as many police officers die every year of stress-related illnesses as die of all job-related injuries combined. This text is intended to help reduce these statistics by assisting human service professionals in coping with the stress to which they are exposed each day.

S. G.

# Dedication

To Joanne, my wife and friend, whose love and support mean more to me than anything else in the world.

S. G.

To my nieces and nephews: Peter, Robert, and Joya Valletutti; Lorna, Gabriel, and David Rivadeneira; and Patty Mayrsohn.
To my wife, Billie, for her encouragement and support.

P. V.

# Stress
## and the
# Helping Professions

# Chapter 1
# Introduction

In 1974, the president of the Blue Cross and Blue Shield Associations referred to stress as "one of the most common problems ... that attacks all of us, at all ages" (McNerney, 1974). Since that time, extensive research has been conducted and numerous articles have been written analyzing and describing the impact of stress on the average citizen.

There are almost as many definitions of stress as there are articles and opinions on the subject. McNerney defines it as "your body's physical, mental, and chemical reactions to circumstances that frighten, excite, confuse, endanger, or irritate you" (1974). Stress has also been defined as an external, noxious force that exerts undesirable and unpleasant effects on an individual (Graham-Bonnalie, 1972).

Most people recognize the effects of stress in the form of negative tension or annoyance caused by someone or something at work, at home, or on the road in between. Few people, however, realize that stress may also generate a positive reaction to a stimulus. The positive effects of stress often drive an individual to achieve and to test his or her potential to its maximum.

Dr. Hans Selye, President of the International Institute of Stress in Montreal, has spent more than 40 years studying the impact of stress on the human body. He defines stress simply as "the nonspecific response of the body to any demand made on it" (Selye, 1976), and notes that some stress is not only good but is essential to daily functioning. He concludes that it is impossible to avoid stress in daily living and that the complete absence of stress is achieved only in death.

Stress is much more than nervous anxiety, as most people believe. It is a *physical, mental, or emotional reaction resulting from an individual's response to environmental tensions, conflicts, and pressures.* A person's reaction to such stressors may be clearly visible, or it may be so subtle that he or she is unaware of their effect.

## THE IMPORTANCE OF UNDERSTANDING STRESS

Stress, whether its effects are positive or negative, causes a reaction within the body. It affects the cardiovascular, digestive, and musculoskeletal systems. Stress may also affect a person's ability to cope with the normal anxieties of daily life. Research has identified stress as a primary cause of headaches, backaches, indigestion, nausea, heart attacks, hypertension, ulcers, colitis, constipation, diarrhea, diabetes, allergies, and arthritis. It has also been linked with psychosomatic illnesses, enuresis, anorexia nervosa, and alcoholism.

For the average citizen, the sources or causes of stress are many and varied. Finances, education, sexual relationships, children, professional and promotional opportunity, and rush hour traffic may all be sources of stress.

In all stress situations, positive or negative, people respond. They adapt or adjust to the stimuli. The common cold, for example, is a source of stress. The average person responds physiologically by creating antibodies to fight the invading microorganisms. The victim of the "cold bug" usually reduces his or her physical activity, often remaining in bed or taking a day or two to stay home from work. The victim fights back, drinking liquids, taking aspirin, and contacting a physician if necessary.

Elmer Green, a well-known researcher in the area of holistic health, has noted that the effect of stress is not actually determined by the stress itself but rather by the way in which people view and handle it. Those people who react negatively to stress or who are unable to cope with stress become victims of distress and are most likely to succumb to the mental, physical, and emotional ills listed above.

As a rule, people react poorly to negative stimuli. These adverse, stress-inducing stimuli are commonly called negative stressors. The death of a spouse, an argument with a close friend, receiving a failing grade in a course, and losing sleep are all negative stressors that usually evoke negative responses.

People who have difficulty in coping with stress also may react negatively to positive stressors. A wedding, a job promotion, a visit from close friends, and the purchase of a new home are stressors generally associated with happy and joyful responses. To many people, however, they may be as devastating in their effects as negative stressors.

Environmental stressors may also evoke negative responses even though the individual affected may be totally unaware of their existence. Toxins, pollutants, food additives, and excessive exposure to the elements are a few environmental stressors.

Holmes and Rahe of the University of Washington conducted a study on how people adjust to stress. They identified 43 "life events" that cause stress and gave each a value in relation to the impact or strength of the event and the demand on a person to adjust or adapt. Table 1 presents their Social Readjustment Rating Scale (Holmes and Rahe, 1967).

The Holmes and Rahe Scale, based on work with over 5000 persons, clearly shows the impact of positive stressors. Marriage was given a mean value of 50, a business adjustment was given a rating of 39, and a change in church activities was given 19. All may be viewed as positive and routine activities, but all require some degree of readjustment (Holmes and Rahe, 1967).

Stress exists, to some degree, in almost everything a person does or will do throughout life. Stress needs to be understood because of its potential to disrupt, limit, or, ultimately, end a person's day-to-day functioning. Individuals are constantly adjusting and readjusting as they cope with stress.

## STRESS IN THE HELPING PROFESSIONS

Understanding stress is of particular importance to people who serve in the human service or helping professions. Attorneys,

Table 1. Social Readjustment Rating Scale

| Life event | Mean value |
| --- | --- |
| 1. Death of spouse | 100 |
| 2. Divorce | 73 |
| 3. Marital separation | 65 |
| 4. Jail term | 63 |
| 5. Death of a close family member | 63 |
| 6. Personal injury or illness | 53 |
| 7. Marriage | 50 |
| 8. Fired at work | 47 |
| 9. Marital reconciliation | 45 |
| 10. Retirement | 45 |
| 11. Change in health of family member | 44 |
| 12. Pregnancy | 40 |
| 13. Sex difficulties | 39 |
| 14. Gain of new family member | 39 |
| 15. Business adjustment | 39 |
| 16. Change in financial state | 38 |
| 17. Death of close friend | 37 |
| 18. Change to different line of work | 36 |
| 19. Change in number of arguments with spouse | 35 |
| 20. Mortgage over $10,000 | 31 |
| 21. Foreclosure of mortgage or loan | 30 |
| 22. Change in responsibilities at work | 29 |
| 23. Son or daughter leaving home | 29 |
| 24. Trouble with in-laws | 29 |
| 25. Outstanding personal achievement | 28 |
| 26. Spouse begins or stops work | 26 |
| 27. Beginning or end of school | 26 |
| 28. Change in living conditions | 25 |
| 29. Revision of personal habits | 24 |
| 30. Trouble with boss | 23 |
| 31. Change in work hours or conditions | 20 |
| 32. Change in residence | 20 |
| 33. Change in schools | 20 |
| 34. Change in recreation | 19 |

(*continued*)

Table 1. (*continued*)

| Life event | Mean value |
|---|---|
| 35. Change in church activities | 19 |
| 36. Change in social activities | 18 |
| 37. Mortgage or loan less than $10,000 | 17 |
| 38. Change in sleeping habits | 16 |
| 39. Change in number of family get-togethers | 15 |
| 40. Change in eating habits | 15 |
| 41. Vacation | 13 |
| 42. Christmas | 12 |
| 43. Minor violations of the law | 11 |

physicians, teachers, nurses, social workers, police officers, counselors, and clergymen and women are among the many professionals who provide human services. In each of these fields, as well as in many others, conditions exist that may exacerbate the negative effects of stress on individual practitioners.

There are certain characteristics associated with the human service professions that increase the vulnerability of practitioners to the negative effects of stress. In general, human service professionals:

1. Become deeply involved in the lives and well-being of others, whether they are clients, patients, students, or congregants.
2. Wield some degree of control in directing the activities of others.
3. Are regularly exposed to human grief, deprivation, struggle, and failure, as well as to the inability of others to cope adequately with their daily functions—mental, physical, or emotional.
4. Spend long, usually irregular, hours accomplishing specific job tasks.
5. Are expected to or expect to perform a variety of activities, many of which may not be directly related to his or her specific function. For example, a physician must be able to pro-

vide counseling; a teacher may be required to respond to the social/familial needs of a student; a police officer may be required to administer emergency medical aid to an injured person.

6. Are expected to be familiar with and able to make referrals to a variety of resource agencies. A social worker may be required to understand the procedures of 10 or 20 agencies that may be called on to render assistance to a client.

In dealing with people, human services professionals have far greater personal interaction and more in-depth knowledge of their clients' personal values and attitudes than do most other workers who provide various services to consumers. Although salespersons, plumbers, chefs, and secretaries all serve the public in some manner, the services that they provide do not require insight into the needs, desires, and characteristics of the individuals they serve. In addition, their work generally is better defined, their control over the lives of their client is minimal, their exposure to human grief may be nonexistent, and their knowledge of service agencies is unnecessary.

In general, members of the human services professions are required to serve too many people, with too few resources at their disposal. In one metropolitan center, for example, a group of four probation officers received new cases at a rate of 60 each month, with no additional fiscal or human support. Elementary school teachers in many areas of the country continue to teach classes of 35, 40, or 45 students despite the increasing demands resulting from mainstreaming and its resultant greater student heterogeneity. Physicians and members of the clergy work 18-hour days in many communities. The prevailing practice of working to assist as many people as possible while simultaneously providing the best possible service is one of the primary stressors within the human services field.

To further compound this situation, reductions in government revenues and in governmental spending at all levels have reduced the likelihood that human service professionals will experience relief in the future. Additional stress is caused as human service practitioners anticipate increased workloads in already overcrowded systems. As the volume of work increases in private industry, so do incoming revenues: supply and demand go hand in hand. In the human service fields, however, there is little correlation between the volume of work or productivity, the demand for service, and incoming revenues.

*Experiment* ✕ In 1978, the Brown University conducted a study that confirmed a higher incidence of stress-related illnesses among people whose jobs require that they bear significant responsibility for the well-being of others (Anderson, 1978). This is particularly significant when considering the number of people currently employed in the human service fields. Although no exact accounting is available, estimates show that the number of people currently employed in the helping professions exceeds several million. The human services fields include people employed in private industry and government service as well as many who are self-employed.

The variety of fields within the human services area makes gathering precise data an awesome task. This task is complicated by the range of employment, from private and public service to self-employment, that exists within these fields.

## PROBLEMS RESULTING FROM
## A LACK OF KNOWLEDGE REGARDING STRESS

✕ [Like the doctor's daughter who is always sick or the police officer's son who is always in trouble with the law, members of the human service fields often become candidates for their own services. So much of their energy may be dissipated in treating and coping with the mental, physical, and emotional ills of others, that there is little psychic or physical energy left for personal care and development beyond the basic necessities.] Thus their own well-being receives scant attention.

Regarding the impact of stress on all people, Dr. Thomas H. Budzynski, of the Biofeedback Institute in Denver, stated that, although stress is a relatively new concept in our culture, "most of us will die of disorders related to our inability to cope successfully with it" (1978). By not associating the emotional and physical problems occurring in the helping professions with stress and by continually making the care of self a second or third priority, most people employed in the human service fields dramatically increase their chances of succumbing to stress-related disorders.

Holmes and Rahe applied their Social Readjustment Scale to the identification of people who are susceptible to stress-related illness. For 2 years, they maintained specific data on residents of Seattle. They rated each of the residents according to the life-event units on the Scale. The scores of the residents were calculated for a 1-year period. Of the people who scored 300 points or more on the Scale, 86% experienced some major illness. Of those people who scored between 150 and 300 points, 48% became ill. Of those scoring less than 150 points, only 33% experienced a noticeable change in health (Holmes and Rahe, 1976).

Selye once termed stress the "speedometer of life," noting that it is the "sum of all the wear and tear caused by any kind of vital reaction throughout the body at any one time" (1976). He determined that stress had a cumulative effect on the body:

> Many people believe that, after they have exposed themselves to very stressful activities, a rest can restore them to where they were before. This is false. Experiments on animals have clearly shown that each exposure leaves an indelible scar, in that it uses up reserves of adaptability which cannot be replaced. It is true that immediately after some harrassing experience, rest can restore us almost to the original level of fitness by removing fatigue. But the emphasis is on the word "almost." Since we constantly go through periods of stress and rest during life, just a little deficit of adaptation energy every day adds up ... it adds up to what we call aging. (Selye, 1976)

Many people within the human service fields are exposed to harrassing experiences daily. As a result of continued exposure to these experiences, some practitioners find that their ability to cope with stress diminishes. This may result in job burnout as well as in mental and physical illness.

To ignore the impact of stress—that is, to ignore the illnesses and other signs that demonstrate that the body and mind are reacting to stressors—is a mild and slow form of suicide. As Seyle points out, "more and more people are killed by disease-producers which cannot be eliminated by the methods of classic medicine. An ever-increasing proportion of the human population dies from the so-called wear-and-tear diseases, which are primarily due to stress" (Selye, 1976).

Characteristically, practitioners in the human service field do not cease their professional activities at the end of a normal work day. A dedicated schoolteacher, for example, is not a 9:00 AM to 3:00 PM employee, as some people might believe. The competent teacher will arrive at school early to prepare for the day's lessons, conduct classes for 5 or 6 hours, and then prepare the classroom for the next day. During the day's classes, the teacher will evaluate each student's individual needs and will, when possible, program activities to meet these needs. The teacher will face myriad disciplinary problems, parental concerns, and administrative details. It is a full and stressful work day.

An effective teacher's day does not conclude with his or her departure from the school, however. At home, lesson plans must be created and tests and papers must be graded. The teacher's "off-duty" time may also be spent preparing report cards and making follow-up telephone calls or visiting parents who are home only in the evening. If a particularly pressing or serious problem exists with an individual student, it may plague the teacher's thoughts throughout the evening, disrupting sleeping, eating, and personal interactions.

The vulnerability of members of the human service fields to the negative effects of stress is great. The humanistic elements of most jobs within these fields, such as the dedication of the individual and the assumption of responsibility for others, combined with the more tangible elements, such as long hours, low pay, and limited advancement opportunities, make the study of stress vital to personal health and well-being.

## DESTROYING SOME MYTHS ABOUT STRESS

Because the study of stress is a relatively new endeavor, many misconceptions exist that lead people to react inappropriately in their efforts to cope with daily stressors. An examination of these misconceptions reveals many of the facts that are now known regarding stress.

### All stress is bad or negative.

The most common misconception about stress is that its effects are all bad or negative. A multi-billion dollar industry has been built on this concept, and relaxation devices, tranquilizers, and therapy programs have emphasized the negative aspects of stress. Although these devices and programs may be effective, in some cases, in coping with the negative effects of stress, they also succeed in distorting the public's view of stress. Selye points out that stress is, in fact, the "spice of life" (1976). It exists, to some degree, in everything a person does, and its effects are positive as well as negative. According to Selye, it is impossible to avoid stress in daily life, and the complete absence of stress would occur only with death. It is positive stressors, on the job and at home, that motivate a person to greater achievement.

### Stress should be avoided at all cost.

Since stress is present, in different degrees, in everything a person does, it is impossible to avoid. To avoid stress successfully would require the complete absence of any form of activity. Although learning about stress may help a person to recognize and avoid some negative stressors, there is no way an individual can completely eliminate such stressors. To attempt to do so would be futile.

### Tranquilizers and drugs may be used to eliminate stress.

No drug or tranquilizer is capable of eliminating stress. Rather, they are used to lessen the effects of stress on the individual. In some cases, the drug taken may mask rather than diminish the effect of stress. In such cases, many researchers and physicians believe more harm than good is accomplished.

## To avoid stress, a person's aim should be to work as little as possible.

Work itself does not cause stress. |Stress on the job is generally due to the way in which individuals react to stressors that exist within their work environment.| Some jobs or professions involve a significantly greater number of stressors than others. Effective use of leisure or nonwork time is one way to cope with the effects of stress; however, the most enjoyable leisure time generally follows a vigorous, lengthy, or "stressful" work period. A person will enjoy leisure to its fullest after maximum energy is expended in work that he or she enjoys.

## The highest degree of stress is most common in professions that require an individual to work long hours, to maintain a high degree of responsibility, and to cope with maximum pressure on a routine basis.

The opposite of this statement is sometimes true. Hours worked, degree of responsibility, and daily pressure do not have as much impact on job satisfaction as do opportunity to use skills and to participate in decision-making processes. The University of Michigan's Institute for Social Research confirmed that assembly line workers, who suffer from boredom and lack of participation in decision-making processes, tend to experience greater stress on the job than successful executives, who work long hours and assume major responsibilities. People employed in the human service professions are in an awkward position. They bear certain characteristics common to both the successful manager and the assembly line worker. They work long hours and hold positions of responsibility, but are often subjected to long periods of boredom and have little input into the policies that guide them. Consider the police officer or the nurse who might work a shift from midnight until 8:00 AM, performing only routine tasks.

**People at the top of their profession are
most likely to suffer heart attacks due to job stress.**

The Cornell University Medical College conducted a study of 270,000 men of all ages and determined that those who had risen to executive positions had a lower heart attack rate than those who were in mid-management or first-level positions. Among those studied, executives experienced only 60% of the expected incidence of heart disease (1979). There is no correlation, according to the study, between the achievement of success and the incidence of job-related heart disease.

**Stress affects only adults.**

Young children who are upset because they have fought with a friend or have lost a favorite toy are as stressed as adults who have had an argument with an employer or who have had some valuable item stolen. The stress experienced by children is real, although their techniques for coping may be different than those of adults. The parent who tells a child not to worry about the loss of the toy because it is not important is as ineffective in dealing with stress as a police officer who tells the victim of a theft that he or she may as well forget about the stolen item because it is not likely that it will ever be recovered.

**The nature of stress within the
human service professions is unique.**

There are very few truly "unique" characteristics within the human service professions. The nature of stress within these fields is not unlike the stress experienced in many other professions. However, the degree of stress or the number of stressors experienced within a given period may set the human service fields apart from other professions. A correctional officer, for example, is exposed to an element of danger every day, as is a truck driver and an assembly line worker. There is a significant difference, however, which causes a correctional officer to experience greater stress. The truck driver and the assembly line worker are invariably well aware of the dangers to which they are exposed. A drunk driver crossing an intersection, a piece of faulty equipment, or a shifting load are all obvious sources of danger. For a correctional officer, the source of danger is usually unknown. Which prisoner will suddenly turn violent? Who has smuggled a weapon into a cell? Unknown dangers and professional risk taking are sources of stress peculiar to certain human service fields. A physician or nurse who must make a decision that may determine whether a person lives or dies or a social worker who must decide whether or not a family will receive a subsidy are facing stressors that do not exist in professions that do not involve providing direct human services.

## PROVIDING DIRECT SERVICE TO PEOPLE

Just as there are many myths about stress, there are misconceptions and distortions about the human service or helping professions. The realization that many of the common beliefs about these professions are, in fact, distortions has led many practitioners to become disillusioned early in their careers.

As a result of civil and campus strife in the mid- and late 1960s and the interest in human welfare generated during the Kennedy and Johnson administrations, new energy was directed toward improving those services designed to improve the life of most Americans. New social welfare programs, improved health care services, and a more efficient criminal justice system were among the goals articulated during this period.

Millions of dollars in federal, state, and local funds were spent on implementing new programs in many human service areas. Thousands of new jobs became available. Educational institutions implemented new curricula designed to prepare students for entry into the human service fields.

Many people attracted to the human service fields looked forward to devoting all their time to providing service directly to people. In many cases, however, they found that they spent much of their time seeking additional funds to provide these services, coordinating activities with other practitioners and agencies, and preparing mountains of paperwork to support their actions. Thus, practitioners in many of the human service fields were rapidly exposed to the stress associated with disillusionment. For example, an enthusiastic college graduate selected to teach a third grade class in a modern elementary school was introduced to a system that required that she teach her students to perform successfully on standardized tests. Her desire to provide individualized instruction and to implement the techniques she had learned just a few months earlier while in college had to take second place to the curriculum goals of the school as they related to the standardized testing process.

A newly hired social worker, employed by a state social services system, regarded his interactions with the families he served as private because of the tradition of privileged information in the professional/client relationship. He learned quickly that the information he compiled, much of which was given to him in confidence, was freely shared among other social workers in that and other agencies.

A recreation supervisor assigned to the task of implementing after-school programs for inner-city youth was enthusiastic about the schedule she had developed since it served the very young as well as older teens. Approximately 2 weeks after her programs began, she was informed by the local school officials that the building she used would be closed at 5:00 PM each day because of a shortage of maintenance funds.

In each of these cases, the system that initially attracted the professionals toward public service caused them to be disillusioned. Their efforts to provide direct service to people in need became cluttered with administrative red tape. Their enthusiasm waned as their exposure to negative stress increased.

Providing direct service to people is also made difficult by reduction in governmental funds. State and local jurisdictions that began programs through 3-, 5-, and 10-year federal grants have failed, in many cases, to continue the programs. Other jurisdictions have continued programs but at reduced funding levels. The human service practitioner often faces a situation in which the number of clients or users has increased while the money required to provide service has decreased.

In one school breakfast program, for example, a large, metropolitan city began providing warm meals to young children who were not assured of a balanced breakfast at home. Although the program was not without its problems, it was generally considered successful. Thousands of young people were being fed each morning. Because of administrative difficulties and declining federal funds, the program was reduced to serve only a few sections of the city. Like most major cities in the United States, the local budget was too small to fund the breakfast program completely. A small amount of federal money would trickle into the city from time to time to support the program on a small scale, but funds were never again provided to open the program to all of the students in need, to the frustration of those people given the responsibility of providing the service.

## MANAGING AND BEING MANAGED

Administration and management within the human service fields are areas in which the number of stressors mount daily. Whether it is a doctor who must complete his or her patients' records, a supervising teacher who must write evaluations on members of his or her teaching team, or a police sergeant who must discipline a subordinate officer for using excessive force, managerial chores are generally viewed as a necessary evil within the helping professions rather than a necessary endeavor.

Among many human service workers in government agencies, the climb to managerial or supervisory posts may have been dictated by a desire for increased earning potential. After a given number of years in government service, an employee must either move to a higher-grade position, often in mid-management, or reach a peak in earnings. For those who do not move on, only annual cost-of-living increases may be expected. This situation exists in some nongovernmental agencies and organizations as well.

For a practitioner who becomes an administrator within an organization, a number of changes take place and stress typically accompanies change/ He or she will be called on to implement administrative decisions that may create new difficulties for the practitioners directly involved in providing services to the client. A conflict may arise between the individual's desire to provide service in the most effective and efficient way possible and his or her desire to successfully complete assigned administrative chores. The administrator or manager may undergo stress when employees fail to understand a new policy or budgetary decision. At the same time, an employee may become angered at management's failure to understand the needs of the clients, students, or patients needing service. This lack of understanding and conflict are inherent in the system.

However, within the human service professions, first-level practitioners do often play a more significant role in determining administrative direction than do employees in industries that focus primarily on products. One goal of participative management in the human service fields is the creation of better understanding among administrators and their employees. Dale Yoder, Professor of Economics and Industrial Relations at the University of Minnesota, wrote:

> Managing people in a free society is a necessarily complicated process. In democratic societies, human beings are largely self-managing. Men make their own decisions as to when and where they will find employment. They are not allocated and employed without regard to their own wishes. Their desires and aspirations as well as society's stated goals and policies with respect to employment are major determinants in modern employment. Hence labor managment in present-day industry necessarily involves numerous complications and problems not encountered in managing other factors in production. In essence, democratic manpower management means participation and voluntary cooperation ... participation by intelligent, informed employees in many decisions with respect to their own employment. This requirement in itself creates many complications, for it necessitates sharing with employees many responsibilities formerly held unilaterally by employers. (Yoder and Heneman, 1958)

The complexities of management are nowhere more intricate than in the human service fields. Judgments and decisions may affect the lives of thousands of people. A simple managerial error could cost hundreds of thousands of dollars in funds. Whereas a director, administrator, superintendent, or principal makes management decisions affecting budget and policy, first-level field practitioners make managerial-related decisions that may have a significant impact on the quality of service to their assigned core of users. For all of the people in the management system, the primary goal remains service to the public. The realization that all people will not be served as adequately as possible because of limited resources places additional strain on everyone involved in providing services.

In addition to these human elements, stress may result from a lack of education and experience in administrative technique. Few of the managers serving human service agencies have been trained for these positions. Rather, they received their education and the bulk of their experience as field service practitioners. The police administrator was a street cop, the hospital's director was a physician, and the supervisor of a state's social services office was a social worker.

Although the system of employing field practitioners as managers has merit, it often prohibits implementation of innovative managerial techniques. Few managers in the human service fields are sufficiently experienced to analyze the cost-benefit ratio of their programs, to develop and implement a system of management by objectives, or to develop a master plan that dictates future directions. Neither their training nor their experience have given them the proper tools with which to function in the administrative area (Mercer and Koester, 1978).

## IDENTIFYING PUBLIC NEED

One of the primary tasks facing administrators and field practitioners within the human service professions is the identification of client needs that must be addressed. A physician must make a careful diagnosis in order to properly plan effective treatment. College administrators and instructors must identify needs within the job market so that instruction remains relevant.

Many human service practitioners experience a high degree of stress as they attempt to prioritize the services that they will provide. When dealing with the well-being of people, it is difficult to decide that certain services will not be provided. Yet, a priority system is vital to providing the best possible service to the largest number of users in the most effective manner possible.

In *Public Management Systems* (1978), Mercer and Koester outlined the following eight types of public service needs:

1. **Perceived/Wanted/Needed** Police service is one example of this type of need. The public sees a need for, and wants, police service on a 24-hour basis. In addition, the rising crime rate generally supports a need to have it. This represents the most significant type of human service need.
2. **Perceived/Wanted/Not Needed** Garbage collection is a service that most people perceive as a real need, and that most people also want. However, in some communities, it is not a vital need since it does not always cause a health or environmental hazard.
3. **Perceived/Not Wanted/Needed** The public perceives that there is a need for racial integration in the schools, but they do not want court-ordered busing in order to fill the need. There is a need to have busing, however, since the courts have ruled that integration must be accomplished (a court-dictated need).
4. **Perceived/Not Wanted/Not Needed** Transferring water from one section of a state to another may be perceived as a valid need by all of the residents of the state. The residents that have the water, however, may not want to provide the tax revenue to do so. Their lack of support demonstrates a lack of need on their part, even though the people without the water may demonstrate the opposite.
5. **Not Perceived/Wanted/Needed** Most people are not aware of air pollution, and therefore, do not perceive the need for an

air quality control program. Through their purchases of automobiles, they demonstrate that they want and support air quality control devices. Through implementation of government programs, as dictated by law, the need is established.

6. **Not Perceived/Wanted/Not Needed** Most citizens do not perceive an actual need for a public zoo, although most would clearly want one in their community. There is no real need for the zoo either.

7. **Not Perceived/Not Wanted/Needed** Most people do not visit the areas of their community that require rehabilitation of housing. Similarly, most people do not want to spend their tax dollars to repair worn out, often unoccupied houses. Planners and government officials, however, may see a vital need to rehabilitate an area, with interest in its long-range implications for the well-being of the community.

8. **Not Perceived/Not Wanted/Not Needed** This category usually includes special projects of certain agencies or individuals. There is rarely a publicly perceived need for the project and, in general, the public does not want the project. The need usually exists only in the thoughts of the individual sponsor or special interest group.

In almost every community, projects exist to meet each of these eight categories of public need. Since determining needs, however, is one of the major responsibilities and, at the same time, one of the primary stressors within the human services field, there are always conflicts. For example, one person's favorite program is disliked by another because it is too restrictive.  Public opinion and sentiment and that of special interest groups may coincide to dictate implementation of a program one week. Then, because of the sentiment and opinion of others who are opposed to it or because of flaws in its implementation, its demise may be dictated the next. Political sentiment may have the same impact on the development and discontinuation of human services programs, resulting in energetic efforts by managers and field practitioners to please those politicians involved in budgetary and legislative decision making.

## SUMMARY

Providing needed services to people is a complex, time-consuming, costly, and most stressful task. The human service professional is exposed to negative stressors on a daily basis, often resulting in disillusionment and job burnout. The specific stressors that accompany the task of providing services to people are compounded by increased demands for service and declining fiscal resources. Gaining an awareness of the nature of stress in the human services fields will not eliminate those experiences that cause stress, but such knowledge, combined with an awareness of techniques for coping with job stress, may significantly reduce the negative effects. Such a reduction in the negative effects of stress may subsequently enhance the provision of services to the public by providing the human services worker with improved health and an improved work environment. It is toward this end that the following chapters are directed.

# Chapter 2
# Causes of Stress to the Human Service Practitioner

There are many causes of stress in people, and they may be viewed as both positive and negative. In the Holmes and Rahe (1967) Social Readjustment Scale, 43 life events that result in stress were cited, including a vacation, a change in eating habits, and marital reconciliation. Other sources include excessive smoking, sudden emotional shock, concern over the well-being of family members, and relocation to assume a better-paying job. Thus, every individual is exposed to some degree of stress every day.

For the human service professional, stress may be caused by a lack of support services, excessive or irregular work hours, or lack of cooperation from a client, patient, or student. Stress may also be caused by a lack of participation in an agency's planning activities or excessive time spent in administrative meetings. A lack of decision-making authority, constant exposure to human grief, and shift work are also part of the long list of stressors to which the human service professional is exposed regularly.

Unlike many other professions in which job tasks are clear to each employee, the human service field often requires that practitioners make decisions regarding tasks they are to accomplish. For example, a basic goal of the physician is to treat his or her patients; however, the nature of the treatment must be determined on a case-by-case basis. The police officer, whose basic task is to maintain public order, may refer one family involved in a domestic dispute to counseling and may make a criminal arrest in dealing with another. Determining the tasks to be accomplished as they relate to each client, student, or patient is an awesome and stressful responsibility.

## STRESS FACTORS INHERENT IN THE PROFESSIONS

### Role Ambiguity

For many practitioners in the human service fields, the provision of needed services is rife with ambiguity and conflict. What right do practitioners have to intervene in the lives of those to be served? What responsibility must clients assume for the cost of needed services? At what point should referral to another agency or practitioner be made? How close should the relationship between client and practitioner become? These questions are but a few of those that often obscure the role of the human service professional.

Consider the role of the social worker who receives a complaint from a local hospital or a classroom teacher about possible child abuse. The social worker determines the legal basis for intervention, as dictated by state and local law and by the policies of the agency. During the initial review of allegations, thought must be given to referring the event for legal intervention or action or maintaining it completely within the authority of the social services agency. The social worker determines whether agencies such as the police department, health department, child welfare service, or courts should be involved in the situation. Consideration is given also to the effects of removing the child from the home, the impact of a criminal arrest, and the amount of time needed to obtain court documents.

The classroom teacher who recognizes that a student is having difficulties within his or her home also encounters a variety of questions. Should the parents of the child be contacted in an effort to resolve the concerns of an informal basis? Should the school's administrative staff or an external social services agency be contacted? Should the situation be ignored completely?

Traditionally, the tasks to be accomplished by many members of the human service professions have been defined in broad, general terms. Some of the duties and responsibilities taken from the job description forms of several public human service agencies are:

Responding to requests for service from the public
Evaluating the need for follow-up services
Providing in-home counseling as required
Maintaining public order

Each of these broad task descriptions is open to varied interpretation by the human service practitioner.

The lack of clear, precise tasks is evident in the field of social work. In discussing social action and social work, Benjamin E. Youngdahl of Washington University stated:

> One fundamental, basic question which faces us and which remains unanswered is this: "Are we one profession or do we encompass within the term social work two or three or four different professions?" We have evaded this question for a number of years, and thus have failed to arrive at an answer. We have tried to define ourselves and to delimit the areas in which we work and the methods and skills that we use. To be sure, we do agree on a common core, but when we go beyond that we seem to shoot off in various directions. When we attempt to define ourselves, we either get so specific as to define only a part of our present selves, or we get so general and diffuse as to make our definition meaningless. We agree pretty much on our goals, but a good deal less on methods. (Youngdahl, 1966)

Poorly defined tasks are the primary cause of role ambiguity. Disparity between what an individual thinks he or she should be doing and the intent of his or her superiors remains a major stressor in many human service professions.

Role ambiguity may also exist in those fields in which tasks are clearly defined but not clearly delimited. The individual practitioner in this situation understands where his or her job begins but not where it ends—that is, the point at which the practitioner relinquishes responsibility for providing service. Harry Levinson, an authority on stress and emotional health in industry, noted that "in a competitive culture, where problems of rivalry are acute and where men feel keenly their responsibilities, many conscientious men will try to cover every eventuality. This means that they may well overwork themselves unnecessarily, sometimes intrude into the work of others, and waste endless hours in protective effort" (Levinson, 1970).

## Role Conflict

In addition to that caused by role ambiguity, emotional strain and tension are also experienced as a result of role conflict. Role conflict generally occurs when there is a discrepancy between the pattern of expectations attached to a given role by the practitioner and that attached by agency managers and clients, patients, or students. It occurs when the individual is required to conform simultaneously to a number of expectations that are mutually exclusive, contradictory, or inconsistent, so that adjustment to one set of requirements makes adjustment to another impossible or, at least, difficult (Anderson and Van Dyke, 1972).

There are four basic areas of role conflict resulting from different patterns of expectation. They involve conflict between the individual practitioner's expectations and those of his or her (1) agency, (2) clients, (3) friends, family, and neighbors, and (4) peers.

Consider the elementary school teacher who believes that students should be allowed to express their feelings, thoughts, and beliefs and has established a standard for open sharing of knowledge, feelings, and attitudes in the classroom. In such a classroom, students may participate in small group activities and generate more noise than generally expected, but their learning in the open classroom may be enhanced as they assume responsibility for their classroom activities and as learning is treated more openly and more holistically. Nevertheless, the school's principal may require that the instructional program follow more traditional patterns, particularly as they affect student behavior. A college professor may have to conform to the demands of a "publish or perish" environment in which the emphasis on scholarly research is often greater than that placed on classroom instruction and where the nature of that research does not reinforce instructional knowledge and competency.

The conflict that exists between the expectations of the practitioner and those of the clients or users is a primary cause of stress in the human service fields. A client's expectations for a practitioner may be based on previous experience, on a combination of reality and fantasy, or totally on fantasy. Old wives' tales, movies, television shows, and the news media contribute to the image of the human service practitioner and, therefore, shape the expectations of a client, patient, or student with regard to that practitioner. For example, many people view physicians as benevolent father figures who possess inordinate powers of diagnosis and healing. Physicians are expected to be infallible practitioners who provide exemplary services to the public. Few people are willing to accept a physician's inability to treat an illness or are willing to seek cures from less traditional sources and in less orthodox ways.

Many people view police officers as rugged, thorough, and emotionally distanced. This image has evolved and been reinforced to a large extent by the macho and unrealistic portrayal of police officers in movies and in television adventure series. The public may not be willing to accept a police officer who expresses sorrow and/or genuine concern at the sight of human suffering. As a result of media portrayal and client expectations, many police officers develop a calloused, cynical approach to the tragedies and the human grief they witness.

Stress may also be caused by a conflict between the role expectations of the individual practitioner and those of his or her family, neighbors, and friends. For example, the neighbors and friends of a member of the clergy may view that individual's life as one filled with personal rewards and happiness. They look to the clergy member for guidance, expecting him or her to remain understanding, calm, and compassionate at all times. Yet, like many other human service professionals, a clergy member is continuously exposed to human grief and suffering in his or her interactions with congregants. By their expectations, the neighbors and friends of the clergy member do not allow that individual to deviate markedly from the idealized image.

The expectations of an individual practitioner held by his or her peers can have an impact as a stressor similar to those held by family, friends, and neighbors. A police officer may be perceived by his or her peers as needing to remain calm and objective in *all* crisis situations. Such peer expectation creates a role that the police officer must fill. Regardless of his or her personal needs or desires, a continuous challenge exists to meet peer expectations.

## Role Overload

Role overload is a stressor in all professions. It occurs in a variety of ways, and involves the individual practitioner's interaction within his or her profession in such a way as to have a negative effect on day-to-day functioning. Role overload may occur when the practitioner works excessive or unusual hours, is burdened with too many tasks to be accomplished in a reasonable amount of time, or is forced to make major decisions on a moment's notice and without proper planning or preparation.

Many of the human service professions require that practitioners work unusual hours. Social workers, physicians, police officers, nurses, ministers, and others often work long hours or are required to work shift rotations. Although most of these persons were fully cognizant of the required work hours on entering the profession, this knowledge does not reduce the stress caused by the real work situation and by working hours different from those of other family members and friends.

In addition to the unusual work hours that are viewed as acceptable aspects of most human service professions, role overload is caused by excessive workloads. The juvenile intake officer who may have responsibility for 150 cases, the nurse who may be working alone on a ward with a large number of patients, and the social worker who may have to make 10 or 12 home visitations in a single day all suffer from role overload. In many human service professions, the problem worsens as demands for service continue while resources decline. This form of role overload results in less than optimal services and, to the dedicated practitioner, is a significant source of stress.

Many practitioners also experience role overload caused by an irregular workload. The family physician who must deal with a large outbreak of flu and the police officer who must deal with a sudden increase in residential burglaries in a specific community are both faced with an uneven workload. Such irregularity in workload may be viewed as a positive stressor if it occurs infrequently. In such cases, the sudden increase in workload offers a change from routine and challenges the practitioner's interests and skills. When the workload increases and decreases suddenly and excessively, however, the practitioner may experience difficulty in planning activities and meeting assigned objectives. The ever-changing and highly unpredictable workload becomes a source of negative stress.

Role overload is also experienced when a human service practitioner is placed in situations requiring major decisions on short notice. For many practitioners crises situations must be resolved rapidly. Decisions are made without opportunity for planning or detailed fact gathering. Decisions that are made on an ad-hoc basis may have significant impact on the lives of others. As with an irregular workload, decision making on brief notice may produce positive stress by challenging the individual's abilities. In excess, however, such decision making becomes a taxing and negative stressor as the human service professional makes far-reaching decisions in professional isolation.

## Responsibility for Others

At the foundation of all of the human service fields is a responsibility for the well-being of others. It is this sense of
responsibility for others that attracts many practitioners to the
helping professions. Historically, the news and entertainment
media, literature, and the educational system have portrayed
the human service worker as a dedicated, hard-working, selfless
individual whose devotion to helping others surpasses devotion
to his or her own family or concern for personal well-being.
Some of the human service fields, such as medicine and law
enforcement, have been glamorized to portray the practitioner
as one whose life is full of excitement and drama in providing
service to others. Although a genuine sense of responsibility
for the well-being of others exists among most human service
workers, attempting to live up to the idealized and glamorized
image fostered by the various media is often another source of
stress.

For some practitioners, the task ideal that attracted them
to the human service field—that is, directly helping others—has
been overshadowed by administrative chores, declining budgets,
bureaucratic red tape, and limited success in helping and
changing the lives of other. Stress occurs as the practitioner
compares his or her role expectations to the reality of day-to-
day functioning. Although most administrative and supervisory
tasks are vital to the successful functioning of an agency,
church/temple, or office, they rarely offer the same sense of
satisfaction to the practitioner as directly interacting with
clients, patients, or students.

## Interaction with Others

All of the professions within the human service field require
interaction among people. The practitioner must deal with
clients, peers, supervisors, subordinates, and members of
support and follow-up agencies and organizations. Stress, both
positive and negative, is a natural consequence of this daily
interaction.

In dealing with clients, the human service professional may experience stress as a result of his or her personal biases. A social worker may experience emotional strain or tension in having to work with people against whom he or she is biased. The practitioner often will mask his or her racial, religious, sex, age, and/or class prejudices in order to perform as effectively as possible. This masking process, i.e., the putting aside of prejudices on a temporary basis, is a source of stress. Stress also occurs when personal prejudices are not masked and surface during interaction with others and when they consciously affect decisions and quality of service.

Interaction with administrators and supervisors is another primary source of stress to the human service practitioner. When interacting with a superior or administrator, the practitioner is generally involved in one or more activities related to planning, work assignments, information processing, disciplinary action, or scheduling. Such administrative interaction is time consuming and is often seen as interfering with direct service to clients. Kroes, Margolis, and Hurrell, in a study of 100 Cincinnati police officers (1974), unexpectedly found that the most significant stressors were those that interfered with or threatened the officers' professionalism in the field. These included being reprimanded by superiors, poor scheduling, particularly as it pertained to appearing in court, undesirable assignments, and weak administrative policies and procedures.

Interacting with resource agencies is a significant source of stress to the human service practitioner. It is in this area that he or she often experiences obstacles in attempting to provide service to his or her clients, students, or patients. The obstacles may be the result of bureaucratic red tape, manpower shortages within the agency, or any number of related problems. Any obstacle to providing service may be a source of stress to the practitioner.

## Involvement in the Planning Process

Many human service workers have little involvement in the planning processes of their agencies. Yet, the policies, procedures, and budgets that are developed by supervisors and administrators in planning sessions significantly affect the day-to-day functioning of these field-level workers. Lack of participation in the organization's planning process becomes a source of stress to the practitioner.

Because of recent studies and trends in private industry, an increasing number of human service agencies and organizations are involving personnel at all levels in the planning and management processes. As Levinson points out:

> When a manager at any level, let alone an executive, takes the time to sit down with those who are reporting to him to ask them how they feel about their work and how it is going, how they feel about what he is doing to facilitate their work, or even what he is doing that may hinder it, how the work might be improved, what the whole picture looks like, and what is necessary to meet the demands on the organization, then people begin to feel respected as human beings. This means that the boss must state the goals and resources, that he must take suggestions and ideas seriously, consider them honestly, allow open discussion of them, and, if additional information is necessary or if decisions have to be referred for the consideration of others, that there be prompt, accurate, and honest feedback about them. (Levinson, 1970)

Involvement of all levels of personnel in the planning process has many benefits besides the reduction of stress. New ideas evolve, both management and field practitioners are educated to needs and concerns within their respective operations, and an understanding of agency goals and objectives is facilitated. For the participative planning process to be successful, however, the roles and limitations of each work group must be clear. Failure to define these may have as negative an effect on morale and performance as no participation in the process. People need to know the boundaries of their participation in planning and management. These boundaries may include an understanding of information that administrators are not able to share and knowledge of budgetary limitations placed on the organization (Levinson, 1970). Failure to involve employees in the planning process and failure to clearly define limitations when they are involved are sources of stress that ultimately affect the individual practitioner's interaction with the people he or she serves.

## Inequities in Pay and Job Status

Within the human services fields, there is great inequity in salary and job status. Although actual salaries vary depending on locale, it is not uncommon, for example, to find a police officer earning a higher salary than a teacher and a teacher earning a higher salary than a social worker. Yet, in most parts of the nation the police officer is required to have a high school diploma, the teacher is required to possess at least a 4-year degree, and the social worker is generally required to possess at least a master's degree.

When comparing salary scales of human service workers to private industry, greater inequity exists. The technician who receives union wage may earn two, three, or four times more than the minister who must work long, irregular hours and who bears responsibility for the well-being of hundreds of congregants. The registered nurse who works in a medical department of a major industrial plant may earn significantly more than the registered nurse who works in a public health clinic, although their functions are essentially the same.

Each individual views pay and job status differently. Whereas some people are satisfied with meeting fundamental financial needs, others are compelled to achieve those comforts that come only with a financial status that goes beyond fundamentals. For some people, salary is the primary incentive for their working. For others, salary is only one item in a long list of motivators that attract them to continued performance within their profession. For those people to whom money is the primary incentive for working, its acquisition generally represents power, achievement, success, personal security, public recognition, and more (Levinson, 1970).

Herzberg notes that job satisfaction derived from salary alone is most common among executives and unskilled workers. Personnel in mid-management, he adds, become dissatisfied with poor salary but generally consider salary as only one small measure of job satisfaction. An equitable salary causes a person to give his or her organization a full day's work, but is little incentive to do more. Recognition and goal attainment along with a good wage provide incentives to an individual to be innovative, to work in a creative manner, and to invest positive energy in accomplishing assigned tasks (Levinson, 1970).

One of the major inequities in pay and job status among human service professionals is the difference between salaries paid to supervisory and administrative personnel and salaries paid to field-level practitioners. Often, the salary paid to an administrator or supervisor is based on a percentage of increase over that paid to the field practitioner. In government service, salary for a supervisor may be increased several grades or steps. This system has been faulted by many for attracting the most effective field practitioners to management, thereby removing them from the people-to-people environment where their services are needed most.

A research report on school system salaries conducted by the National Education Association in 1970 showed a significant difference in the wages paid to classroom teachers and school administrators. Citing mean scheduled salaries, a difference of $6461 was noted between the salary paid to classroom teachers and that paid to high school principals. Over a 25-year career, this difference grows to more than $160,000 (Anderson and Van Dyke, 1972). The conflict that many practitioners face in choosing supervision over classroom instruction in order to achieve a higher salary is a major cause of stress in the field of education. This source of stress exists in most of the human service professions.

## THREE AREAS OF STRESS
## COMMON TO DAILY FUNCTIONING

For the human service practitioner, stress may develop in three areas of his or her daily functioning: field service, administration and supervision, and home and family. For each practitioner, these source areas are somewhat different. For example, in comparing the physician to the schoolteacher, several distinct differences became apparent. The teacher deals in a group environment whereas the physician deals with people on a one-to-one basis. The teacher is responsible to a highly structured hierarchy of management whereas the physician may bear full responsibility for the administration of his or her office. The physician may have long evening hours in the office and may have to be on call 24 hours per day whereas the teacher may have to spend evenings at home preparing lessons for the next day.

## Field Service Stressors

In the area of field service—i.e., performance of basic job tasks—human service practitioners may be exposed to stress in any one or more of the following categories:

Workaholism, irregular work pattern and schedule
Threats, fear, and sources of danger
Narrow scope of authority
Boredom
Burnout
Exposure to human grief

*Workaholism, Irregular Work Pattern, and Schedule* Selye describes workaholism as the behavior of those who work merely as a means of escaping from a life that became stale (Selye, 1976). However, for many human service practitioners, workaholism becomes a way of life because of an obsession to accomplish their tasks—to serve others despite time and budgetary constraints. This sense of dedication is partly self-imposed and partly brought about by the image of the human service worker held by the general public. That is, the work pattern of the human service practitioner is imposed by both a genuine need to provide services and an image that portrays him or her as a tireless, selfless, devoted, and wonderful individual.

Selye also notes that many people work hard and intelligently toward some objective that promises leisure and a more enjoyable life tomorrow, but for them, tomorrow never comes. There is always one more objective that, if accomplished, will provide a greater sense of satisfaction or will provide more leisure for a still elusive tomorrow. When people ignore present satisfaction and look only toward the future, they fall into a workaholic pattern (Selye, 1976).

The work patterns and schedules of many practitioners are dictated by their agency or by their chosen field. The police officer, nurse, and firefighter must work a shift rotation in order to provide service to their clients. Similarly, a physician or a member of the clergy must be available to clients on a 24-hour basis, even though he or she may not be involved in the actual process of providing service. The social worker and the probation officer must provide service to their clients whenever they can, imposing a schedule that is extremely irregular. In each of these situations, stress is present as a result of the work schedule or pattern. How the individual adjusts to his or her work schedule determines whether he or she is affected positively or negatively by this stress.

The techniques made available to the human service worker for planning his or her time and work schedule may also be a source of stress. Without planning, it is impossible to predict, prepare for, and cope with the future (Woolfolk and Richardson, 1978). Planning is the process through which the individual identifies specific needs and how he or she will go about addressing them. For some human service workers, major responsibility for planning must be assumed; for others, most planning is done for them. Negative stress may be experienced in either case, but there are few things that cause more stress to the practitioner than not participating in the planning of field-level activities. A police officer who must follow a directive on the use of force that was developed solely by administrative personnel may hesitate to accept these procedures. The officer would be more willing to accept and follow the directive if he or she had played some role in identifying problems, issues, and alternative solutions regarding the use of force.

**Threats, Fear, and Sources of Danger**  Threats of violence and potential dangers exist in a number of human service fields.

The police officer and firefighter are exposed to danger and threats of violence daily. Although this is a genuine source of stress, both of these practitioners understand that these threats are a part of their daily function. Other practitioners, such as social workers and teachers, generally do not expect threats of or actual violence to be a part of their world of work. Yet, their exposure to violence may be as frequent and as stressful as that experienced by the police officer or firefighter. The teacher who has been assaulted by an angry student or the social worker who must travel to a high crime area alone is exposed to an intense form of stress.

*Narrow Scope of Authority* Negative stress is also experienced when the human service practitioner is not given sufficient authority to make or control decisions that govern how his or her services are provided. In addition to having no involvement in major decision making, limited authority may include having little or no involvement in planning long-range services or no direct involvement in follow-up activities. A uniformed police officer, for example, may gather the initial facts in a case in which a citizen has been victimized. Once these facts are gathered, however, the officer may be required to relinquish responsibility for the follow-up investigation to a criminal investigator. His or her involvement in the follow-up investigation may be minimal.

*Boredom* Boredom is another source of stress within the field operation of a human service practitioner. The nurse who is assigned to a quiet night shift, the social worker who spends long hours waiting for resource agencies to respond to a request for service, and the supervisor who must regularly sit through long administrative meetings all experience boredom. Often, it is during these periods of boredom that the practitioner is prohibited from providing service to those in need.

*Burnout* Excessive boredom is one of the many causes of job burnout, which is another source of stress and one of the primary reasons that people leave the human service fields. Job burnout occurs when a person no longer derives any satisfaction from his or her profession and sees no merit to his or her daily functioning. It affects the individual's performance and, in many cases, his or her behavior. Burnout is both caused by stress and a source of additional stress.

Burnout may be experienced when an individual is assigned to a single function for too long a period or is transferred from one function to another too rapidly. Burnout can be the result of reduced job satisfaction or the result of a lack of recognition and reward for successful accomplishment of assigned tasks. Time-consuming routine tasks and self-doubt are two other causes of job burnout. There are two primary ways in which a practitioner's self-doubt may prohibit continued performance of his or her job—by producing an inability to undertake increased responsibility of which he or she is capable, and by bringing on the feeling of having reached an occupational dead-end and of being destined to remain in the same function for the rest of his or her career (Levinson, 1970). Regardless of the reason, job burnout and the subsequent dissatisfaction with one's profession that follows are among life's most significant stressors.

***Exposure to Human Grief*** Because they are called on to provide services when people are in need, many members of the human service fields are exposed to one or more of the many forms of human grief. For some, this involves direct daily exposure to the negative aspects of life: physical, mental, and emotional. For others, this exposure may be occasional or indirect, as with a supervisor who may be required to approve reports of field practitioners who experience direct contact with citizens. Human grief becomes a strain to the practitioner because, in some cases, the action taken to alleviate the suffering either causes increased grief or exposes the client to a complex and impersonal bureaucratic system. Those cases in which human grief is alleviated efficiently and effectively are not as common as many practitioners would desire. For example, a dentist may become stressed every time he or she must inflict pain. A teacher may feel stress in attempting to gain rapid assistance for a student whom he or she has identified as having a severe learning disorder. In both cases, the practitioner is expected to remain unemotional and objective in order to provide the most effective service possible to the person in need. Having to suppress emotions in the face of human grief is thus another stressor experienced in the human service fields.

## Administrative Stressors

Lourn Phelps of the University of Nevada identified 58 areas of stress related to administration within the criminal justice field. They apply to most of the human service fields, and include lack of recognition for accomplishments, relationships with supervisors, excessive paperwork, lack of training, job security, participation in decision-making, promotions and advancement, lack of coordination, media relations, presence of corruption, and incompetence of leadership (Phelps, 1977).

Much of the stress, frustration, and irritation experienced by human service practitioners is blamed on administrators. The physician may fault the hospital administrator, the police officer may blame the police chief, and the teacher may resent the principal. Many of those areas of stress already discussed as part of the field service are rooted in administrative style, processes, and procedures and in the antipathy felt by field practitioners toward administrators. The following categories of administrative stress are found within most of the human service fields:

Policies and procedures
Work schedules
Excessive paperwork and redtape
Relationship with supervisors
Accountability for decisions made under pressure
Inconsistency among supervisors
Transfer of assignments
Response to public opinion and complaints
Evaluation systems and measures of effectiveness
Organizational rumors
Promotional opportunity and advancement
Responsibility commensurate with authority
Physical resources

There are other areas of administrative stress that are unique to specific human service fields. The police officer, for example, experiences administrative stress when he or she receives repeated summonses to appear in court during off-duty time. The teacher experiences administrative stress when a principal will not support specially designed instructional strategies and procedures that are not traditional.

The types of administrative stress that are common to most of the human service fields are discussed below.

*Policies and Procedures*  The role an employee plays in the development of an agency's policies and procedures will significantly affect the way those policies and procedures are applied in the field. Anderson and Van Dyke (1972) note, "A major reason for involving teachers in policy formulation is that they are the ones who eventually must implement policies. If policies are not acceptable to teachers, they either will find ways of circumventing them or will not make a sustained effort to achieve them. On the other hand, policies which incorporate teachers' views are likely to be implemented with good effort." Negative stress evolves when practitioners do not participate in the policy-making process and when policies are ambiguous.

*Work Schedules*  Most human service professionals anticipate long, often irregular hours on entering their chosen field. Work schedules cause negative stress when they do not adequately meet the needs in the field, interfere with the practitioner's home life too frequently, and/or favor one practitioner over another with no justification. Just as with the formulation of policy, the individual practitioner views his or her work schedule more favorably if he or she has played some role in formulating it. There are some administrative stressors related to scheduling over which the practitioner has little control, even when invited to participate in general scheduling activities with others. For example, the dentist who has allowed a certain amount of time for each patient will experience stress when one patient is in need of an extensive amount of care, thereby disrupting the schedule he or she has planned for working with others.

*Excessive Paperwork and Red Tape* The social worker who must file five or six lengthy forms in order to gain public assistance for a family in need and the public health administrator who must spend 2 or 3 weeks completing a complex grant application both experience negative stress when this volume of papers they must complete interferes with the efficient provision of services to their clients. Most human service professionals must compile written reports on their daily activities and must complete detailed requests for supportive resources or services to assist in meeting the needs of their clients, students, or patients. When completing reports and forms requires excessive time or interferes with providing direct services to clients, the stress that evolves is considered administrative in nature. Currently, the demands made by Public Law 94-142 on special education teachers to prepare individualized education plans (IEPs) is creating great stress.

*Relationship with Supervisors* Human service practitioners may experience a wide variety of stressors through their interaction with supervisors and administrators. Directives that are not clearly understood, performance evaluations, and disciplinary action are all sources of stress associated with supervision. Levinson (1970) notes that there is a mutual frustration occurring between supervisors and dedicated field practitioners. "In all kinds of organizations, colleges and monasteries as well as businesses, the bright young man puzzles, angers, irritates, and frustrates his supervisors" (Levinson, 1970). Similarly, the supervisor frustrates the bright, young worker. This mutual frustration may stem from a lack of an orientation program for the new practitioner, a rivalry between the supervisor and his or her subordinates, a lack of job security for either the practitioner or the supervisor, and/or a lack of challenging tasks at either level (Levinson, 1970). A feeling of frustration in interacting with supervisors and administrators also develops when orders, directives, evaluations, and management styles are inconsistent. One supervisor, for example, may request that reports be completed in one particular way while another may prefer a totally different approach. A schoolteacher may receive support for a particular project from his or her vice-principal and may be criticized for the same endeavor by the principal.

Stress may also develop when a practitioner feels that he or she has greater skill than the supervisor or administrator who is directing his or her program. This form of stress is common when the field practitioner has received a college education and his or her supervisor has gained that position based on longevity, field performance, and/or irrelevant factors such as personal characteristics and political influence. No matter what the reason, the frustration between supervisors and field practitioners has remained a source of stress within the human service fields, as it has in most professions. Anastasi notes

> Despite the many complexities that beset the study of employees' attitudes, one fact that emerges clearly is the importance of supervisory practices. Attention has been focused particularly on the key role of the foreman or first-line supervisor in shaping employee attitudes. ... Surveys of the source of job dissatisfaction have repeatedly shown the behavior of the immediate supervisor to be a major factor. Supervisory behavior has also been found to be significantly related to absenteeism, accidents, grievances, and turnover in different departments. (Anastasi, 1964).

*Accountability for Decisions Made under Pressure* Many practitioners in the human service fields are called on to make decisions in crisis situations. The physician, nurse, police officer, firefighter, minister, social worker, and classroom teacher share responsibility for making decisions under pressure that may have a significant impact on the lives of their clients, patients, and students. How managers view and support such decision making affects the willingness of practitioners to assume this responsibility. For example, Kroes, Margolis, and Hurrell (1974) found that police officers felt more threatened by supervisory reprimand and challenge to their professionalism than by the dangers generally associated with law enforcement. In explaining this source of stress, officers said that they were held accountable for decision making but did not feel that they were supported by supervisors when those decisions were not totally in accord with the agency's administrators.

Along with supervisors, the general public holds most human service workers accountable for the decisions they make. There is a mystique, for example, about physicians. The public expects them to make major decisions about health with only a minimum amount of time for diagnosis. This is particularly true in time of crisis when there is a serious illness or injury that must be treated. This perceived accountability is a primary source of stress for physicians. In a study of more than 2500 physicians, it was found that the incidences of heart ailment was higher among general practitioners and anesthesiologists, who are placed in crisis situations regularly, than among dermatologists, pathologists, and other specialities within the field of medicine. This was attributed to the higher levels of stress to which the former are exposed (Selye, 1976).

*Inconsistency among Supervisors* A significant source of stress to field practitioners is inconsistency among their supervisors and administrators. Different priorities, individual requirements for completion of paperwork, and individual styles of discipline often complicate and weaken the provision of services to those in need by placing the practitioner in a conflict situation. Inconsistencies in supervision may be the result of misinterpretation of agency or organization goals by the individual supervisor. They may also result when the supervisor and the practitioner have perceived the agency's goals differently, although both perceptions may be positive. Conflicts with supervisors and inconsistent supervision are inevitable as long as individuals are allowed to broadly interpret the basic objectives they are to accomplish (Levinson, 1970).

*Transfer of Assignments* Transfers are commonplace in the human service fields. A social worker may be transferred from one district to another, a police officer may be transferred from uniformed patrol to a plainclothes investigative function, and a nurse may be transferred from one ward to another. For some practitioners, transfers are accepted in order to achieve

higher salary levels; for example, a teacher may become an administrator in order to increase his or her wage. Although some
transfers are positive and some are negative, they all produce
stress. Change is the most common cause of anxiety, and even
a change for the better will cause a person to experience some
loss (Levinson, 1970). This may include a loss of environment
in which the practitioner felt comfortable, movement away
from coworkers and friends on whom the practitioner had
grown to rely, or a change in the entire nature of one's work. In
many cases, the professional change is associated with the
agency's or organization's administration, and becomes a
source of stress attributed to people in administrative positions.

*Response to Public Opinion and Complaints*  Since human
service workers serve the public, local sentiment, complaints,
and praise are important in planning future directions. How
user sentiment is addressed within an agency or organization
may be a significant source of stress to the practitioner. A
physician, for example, may take issue with and feel stress over
a decision by the American Medical Association to adopt a new
directive as a result of media complaints arising from a specific
medical practice. There was significant upheaval among many
police officers when major changes were made in national law
enforcement practices following the civil, racial, and campus
strife of the mid-1960s and early 1970s.

In most situations, stress arises when practitioners are not
made aware of how their agency or organization will respond to
citizen complaints, concerns, and suggestions. Some organizations do not have written procedures for addressing citizen concerns and, therefore, each complaint or problem raised by the
public may be handled differently. This also creates stress as
practitioners try to anticipate how their agency will respond.

*Evaluation Systems and Measures of Effectiveness*  Performance evaluations have been termed one of the most contro-
versial issues in personnel management (Wilson, 1977). Evaluation systems have been designed to measure performance and
serve as a guide for salary increases, promotions, transfers, and

disciplinary action. They have been used to assess productivity and to stimulate job performance of administrators, supervisors, and field practitioners. In the past, police chiefs, hospital administrators, and other agency heads have attempted to use a single evaluation system to accomplish a wide variety of tasks. This has caused stress by weakening both the evaluation system itself and its use as a tool in promoting the growth of both the agency and the individual practitioner. Recent trends in management, however, have shown more positive results with an evaluation system that is simple and is designed to accomplish one basic purpose (Wilson, 1977).

A practitioner experiences stress in any evaluation process; however, whether that stress is positive or negative is determined by the quality of the system and how it is to be used. An evaluation given once each year, for example, will be viewed negatively if it is used to determine salary increases and promotional potential. The practitioner views the system positively if a performance appraisal is conducted several times during the year. In this way, he or she feels that opportunities have been provided to make necessary improvements and knows his or her standing in relation to agency requirements. In addition, the way in which the system is administered determines the degree of stress it creates. A practitioner may look favorably on a system administered by several supervisors during the year rather than repeatedly by the same supervisor. In this way, several opinions are reflected and the impact of the personal biases of supervisors is reduced.

In almost all cases, the stress that accompanies evaluations and measurements of performance are attributed to administrators and supervisors within the agency or organization. A weak system, that is, one that does not distinguish effective from ineffective performers, may lead to other personnel problems such as excessive illness among employees and failure to accept new policies and directives. In the human service professions, as in any field, recognition of achievements is essential to the growth and well-being of practitioners. In those fields where there is little or no formal recognition of performance, such as among physicians, dentists, and some members of the ministry, additional stress is experienced. In these fields, recognition of successful performance must come from the practitioner him- or herself.

*Organizational Rumors* In many of the human service fields, organizational rumors cause stress that is characteristically attributed to the administration. The positive or negative nature of this stress will depend on the communications network within the agency or organization. When the communications flow within an agency or among practitioners is weak, rumors develop that may be detrimental to effective functioning. Generally, practitioners in this situation will tend to believe rumors simply because factual information has not been provided by supervision or management. Wilson (1977) states, "The best means of prevention, of course, is widespread dissemination of actual circumstances before rumors can be started. The harmful effect of rumor can be at least partially overcome by adopting a well-developed written directives system, by reducing the vulnerability to rumor through positive training, and by producing information bulletins which simply and pointedly counteract rumors while they are being spread."

*Promotional Opportunity and Advancement* Considering and competing for advancement or promotion in a chosen field may be either a positive or a negative source of stress. In almost all situations, this stress is attributed to the administration. For those practitioners who willingly compete for promotions and who compete within a sound promotional process, the stress that is caused is positive. For those who compete for promotion simply to gain additional salary or who compete in a system that does not consider the individual's performance and growth in an equitable manner, the resulting stress is negative. In the human service fields, many practitioners began their careers wishing to provide direct assistance to people in need for the remainder of their careers. Their aspirations for promotion when beginning their careers may have been slight. They may change their thinking, however, for a variety of reasons. There are those who seek advancement in order to make changes within their field or organization. Some practitioners may seek the financial rewards that accompany promotion and that are not available to the front-line worker. Others may seek the status that accompanies supervisory and managerial positions. Some may seek promotion and advancement simply because they are competitive individuals who make life a series of contests (Woolfolk and Richardson, 1978).

Along with the stress that naturally accompanies a decision to compete for advancement or promotion, the system within which this competition occurs becomes a source of stress to the practitioner. Just as with the evaluation system cited earlier, an equitable system produces less stress than one deemed unfair and prejudicial. Wilson (1977), for example, recommends that evaluation forms not serve as promotional forms but, rather, that promotional potential ratings be prepared for consideration in the process. In this way, the evaluation form simply informs the employee of his or her performance progress, whereas the promotional potential form addresses the information sought in considering an individual for advancement, such as leadership characteristics (Wilson, 1977). This approach also assists in reducing the negative stress experienced by the practitioner who competes in both processes.

*Responsibility Commensurate with Authority* A practitioner in the human service fields may experience stress when his or her duties and functions are not related to the authority with which he or she has been vested. A nurse who is assigned to a clerical function for an extended period of time, a classroom teacher who is assigned to the administrative staff to coordinate a special program, or a social worker who is assigned to develop a grant request are subject to negative stress. Although they have been given significant responsibility in these supportive functions, their primary role is being ignored. If assigned to the supportive function on a long-term basis, they may become rapidly disillusioned. Such assignments are not only stressful to the individual practitioner but are also inefficient. Assigning police officers to clerical tasks, reception desk functions, key-punch operations, and records tasks not only distorts the self-image of the officers but wastes valuable funds since these tasks could readily be filled by civilian employees for lower salaries (Wilson, 1977).

*Physical Resources*   Whereas most sources of stress related to administration are rooted in interpersonal relationships and personnel matters, the physical resources made available to the practitioner may also be a source of physical, mental, and emotional strain and tension. A clergy member whose place of worship is too small to accommodate a growing congregation, a teacher who does not have an office or lounge in which to work during nonteaching hours, and a public health nurse who does not have an office in which to complete reports will experience negative stress. Along with work space, a practitioner is concerned with adequate equipment and resources to complete his or her assigned tasks. When equipment is inadequate or, in many cases, nonexistent, additional stress is experienced. A lack of pens, forms, paper clips, or desk blotters may cause frustration to some people. More serious is the stress experienced by the physician in a clinic that does not have a sufficient supply of vaccine to meet public needs or the teacher who does not have enough textbooks to supply a class. In these cases, the lack of equipment and materials becomes a significant obstacle to successfully completing assigned duties. In each of these situations, the stress-inducing lack of space and equipment is attributed to the agency's or organization's administration.

The areas of administrative stress cited above have been presented as those causing the greatest amount of stress to human service practitioners. The nature of the stress experienced by practitioners will vary in each field and within each agency or organization in a particular field. The nature and degree of administrative stress is contingent on the individuals involved, the resources available to the agency, and the way in which the agency and individuals are viewed by the people they are attempting to serve.

## Home and Family

The stresses an individual experiences within his or her profession affect his or her home life and the lives of his or her family members. The stresses an individual experiences in the home may also influence his or her professional activities. Stress also occurs when one's home life interferes with his or her profession and when professional activities interfere with home and family.

There are five basic areas within the home and family life of the human service practitioner that generate stress:

Professional dedication versus dedication to family
Finances
Education
Personal health
Work status

Each of these areas includes many individual sources of stress experienced by human service practitioners.

*Professional Dedication versus Dedication to Family*   Most people who have a responsive and rewarding home environment want to spend time with their family and friends. They strive to maintain a balance between their desire to work and their desire to recreate and relax at home. For the dedicated human service professional, this desire may be a source of stress. He or she may spend an excessive amount of time working, thereby limiting the amount of time spent with family. Since services to the public may be provided 24 hours per day, 7 days each week, the practitioner may be called on to work odd hours, thereby limiting the family's activities on weekends or during evenings. Stress may be experienced when the family's planning of activities is disrupted repeatedly. The practitioner may also experience stress when involvement in a complex situation requires him or her to ignore family requests and activities. In such cases, the individual's dedication to others causes stress to members of his or her family as well as to him- or herself.

Stress may also be experienced when family members are unfamiliar with the practitioner's professional responsibilities and the nature of his or her work. Without a clear understanding of the practitioner's tasks, family members will be unable to comprehend many of the requirements of the profession. The practitioner, however, may want to shield his or her family from the stresses of the profession and may purposefully withold information from family members. Without understanding and information sharing, negative stress will evolve.

*Finances* Financial strains are generally shared by the practitioner and his or her family. Stress is experienced when the family views salary levels of people in other fields and realizes that parallel positions in the private sector may command a significantly higher wage than is being paid to personnel in public service agencies and organization. With tightening budgets, those human service practitioners working in government-sponsored agencies experience added stress in knowing that future increases in salary may not keep pace with inflation. Stress is also experienced by the family because of the unstable nature of finances in government agencies. For example, in October, 1979, the United States Congress failed to pass a bill releasing funds for payment of salaries to government workers. The bill was delayed because of a clause that had nothing to do with the salary items. The result was a delayed federal payroll that forced some federal workers to function for 2 to 3 weeks without pay. Financial planning in such a situation is difficult, at best.

*Education* Education is important to most human service practitioners for several reasons. Many agencies require educational advancement in order to obtain salary increases and promotions. Public school teachers, for example, may be required to obtain a graduate degree within a specified period of time in order to receive an increase in pay or to maintain their teaching certificate. Other practitioners must pursue advanced education in order to gather current knowledge about their profession. Dentists, for example, must attend workshops and seminars regularly in order to acquire knowledge of current trends and skills in techniques of dentistry. Negative stress is experienced when daily activities do not allow for attending such programs or when sudden crises interfere with classes. For example, a police officer who has changed his or her schedule to accommodate an early evening class at a college may be unable to attend a few classes because of an investigative lead requiring immediate follow-up. A clergy member may be called away from an important seminar because a member of his or her congregation has suddenly become ill. Although the reasons for the interruptions are significant, they do not mitigate the stress engendered over the difficulties in obtaining advanced education. Even greater stress is experienced when the agency or organization requires advanced education but does not make any provision for the practitioner to obtain it. A social welfare agency, for example, may require its employees to complete graduate level coursework in order to be eligible for promotion. It may also require the practitioners to work long hours or shift work and may offer no tuition reimbursement program. The practitioner therefore experiences both scheduling and financial difficulties in meeting his or her agency's requirements.

*Personal Health*   There is a significant link between physical well-being and stress; this is discussed in detail in Chapter 3. For the human service practitioner, stress may be experienced when daily responsibilities do not allow him or her to take care of personal health. A member of the clergy may lead a congregation in worship service even though he or she is quite ill because there is no replacement available. A social worker may leave home to assist a family in need regardless of personal health because he or she judges that the family's needs are more important. Although the need for services may be important, the practitioner experiences negative stress in providing them.

The human service practitioner may also experience stress-related illnesses on a regular basis. These include headache, backache, indigestion, nausea, and hypertension. The dedicated worker may ignore these ailments in order to continue providing services to clients, patients, and students.

*Work Status*   The practitioner's work status may be a

source of negative stress. Police officers, physicians, social workers, and clergy members often function on a 24-hour-per-day, on-call status. They must be available to respond to client needs at any time. They have little relief from their daily work routine unless their agency rotates this 24-hour on-call status among several practitioners.

On-call status also interferes with family planning, since the practitioner must remain available at all times, and this creates stress within the family. For example, the assistant director of a juvenile rehabilitation center must be on-call 24 hours per day because he or she is responsible for the agency's physical plant. Because of a limited staff, this responsibility cannot be shared. A call must be made to the main office every time the family travels. A police officer who is required to carry his or her service revolver when off duty experiences a similar form of stress, and is unable to totally escape from his or her profession.

## SUMMARY

The causes of negative stress to the human service professional are many and varied. Because the practitioner generally deals with meeting the needs of individual people in situations that are unique to those people, he or she bears significant responsibility for determining the tasks to be performed. In making decisions about these tasks, he or she experiences stress in attempting to conform with the policies of his or her agency, the standards of his or her professional organization, and the desires of his or her supervisors and administrators.

The role of the practitioner is often unclear. He or she may experience conflict in determining the precise tasks to be accomplished. Once the tasks are determined, the workload may become excessive in an effort to accomplish them. In accomplishing his or her tasks, the practitioner continually assumes responsibility for the well-being of his or her clients. Yet, although he or she is assigned this significant responsibility, the field practitioner is rarely involved in the planning processes of the sponsoring agency or organization.

For the human service practitioner, stress may develop in three areas of his or her daily functioning: field service, administration and supervision, and home and family. Each of these areas may be divided into several specific categories in which stress may be experienced. Most negative stressors are experienced as a result of interaction with administration and supervision, either directly or indirectly. In all cases, the degree of stress experienced by the human service practitioner is contingent on his or her individual situation at work and at home.

# Chapter 3
# Stress and
# Physical Illness

Most researchers in the field of medicine have acknowledged a direct relationship between illness and stress. Authorities in both the United States and Great Britain have stated that as many as 70% of all patients treated by physicians in general practice may be suffering from conditions that have their roots in unrelieved stress. This supposition is supported by the Thirteenth Report of the World Health Organization, which recognized that certain stress-related diseases can kill an individual as surely as a well-aimed bullet or deadly poison (Blythe, 1973).

## EFFECTS OF STRESS ON THE BODY

All people experience stress. It affects them every hour of every day. For most, the stressors they encounter are positive, and they respond to them favorably. For others, the stressors are negative. How they respond to such stressors determines how they are affected by stress emotionally, mentally, and physically. Since each person responds differently, negative stressors that are harmful to one person may be a positive and stimulating force to another. Even stressors that offers positive challenge to the individual may become overwhelming and may ultimately have the same effects as negative stressors (LaMott, 1974).

People respond to stress in much the same way as an electric power source responds to drains on its energy. A negative stressor is analogous to plugging a frayed wire into an electrical outlet: a negative response is sure to result. A positive stressor is analogous to a new wire and plug being placed into the outlet. The reaction is a positive one, with electricity flowing smoothly from the source to the point of need. A second plug placed in the outlet also receives a positive response, and so might a third. Four or five plugs placed in the outlet, however, will create a strain causing a negative response. The response may be a sudden short circuit or it may be a gradual heating of the wires over a long period of time that eventually erupts into a fire.

For the typical person, the short-circuited system is manifested in physical ailments that may surface in various forms. One of the most dramatic examples of physical reaction to stress was provided by Dr. John C. Cassel of the University of North Carolina in a study of women experiencing motherhood for the first time. Pregnancy and motherhood is recognized as one of the greatest stresses in a woman's life. A woman's identity, social life, and daily functioning change dramatically as she becomes a mother. Dr. Cassel noted that a woman who experiences support and love from her family and friends during the adjustments associated with motherhood and pregnancy experiences a 30% chance of complications during childbirth. This figure climbs to an alarming 90% for the woman who does not receive love and support from her spouse, family, and friends. Pregnancy and motherhood is clearly a situation in which stress affects physical functioning.

Selye defined stress as the "nonspecific response of the body to any demand" (Selye, 1976). He believes that the relationship between stress and a person's physical functioning is so close that the effects of stress on a person can be measured through changes occurring within the structure and chemical composition of the body. He refers to these changes as the "general adaptation syndrome," which includes a measurement of signs of physical damage and manifestations of the body's "adaptive reactions," or mechanisms of defense against stress. He emphasizes that the relationship between stress and a person's physical well-being is great (Selye, 1976).

## Fight or Flight Reaction

Selye notes that the body reacts to stress in a particular way. He terms this the "fight or flight reaction." Whenever the body is threatened or aroused, the fight or flight reaction occurs. As soon as a danger is recognized, the muscles of the body tense for action. The individual is prepared to address the danger, whether it be natural such as sudden inclement weather or unnatural such as an attack by an angry person. He or she may take an aggressive action to cope with the threat or may flee to avoid it entirely. In either case, the body is prepared to respond.

The body's immediate response to this stress results through a reaction of the hypothalamus and the pituitary gland. Signals are sent to all bodily systems to prepare to confront some form of threat to its well-being. The normal thought processes are bypassed and the response of the body is immediate. The body uses increased amounts of stored blood sugar, oxygen flows more rapidly, digestion slows, and blood flows to the heart quickly. Blood pressure rises. The functions of the muscles, heart, lungs, and brain take priority over all other bodily systems until the threat to the body's well-being has passed.

The flight or flight reaction is evoked as a response to all changes effecting the body, positive and negative. They may include exposure to sudden changes in temperature, rage, excitement, and joy. While some responses are more sudden than others, each causes bodily change ranging from dilation of the pupils to a change in the chemical composition of the blood. When an action has been taken to address the situation or event effecting the body, the complex biochemical changes which took place within it end. The bodily functions return to normal, with little or no ill effect. However, when a person is exposed to stress regularly and this fight or flight reaction occurs repeatedly, disorders to the bodily functions may occur. These disorders take their form in headaches, backaches, hypertension, and other stress-related illnesses (Selye, 1976).

Dr. Thomas Holmes, Professor of Psychiatry at Washington University, conducted extensive research on the relationship of stress to physical health. In his early research, he concluded that the onset of certain illnesses such as skin diseases, tuberculosis, heart disease, and some cancers correlate closely with significant changes in a person's lifestyle. Among these lifestyle changes were moving to a new house, divorce, and the death of a close relative. He also noted that not all lifestyle changes had to be significant to cause a physiological reaction. An accumulation of everyday minor changes, such as a family argument, may also have an adverse effect. He noted that there is a highly significant correlation between the degree of change in a person's lifestyle (as ranked on a scale) and various chronic diseases (Blythe, 1973).

In providing a simple explanation for how stress-related disease evolves, Blythe relied on a dictionary definition of the word "tension." Tension is defined as a "pulling strain; stretched or strained state; stretching." Blythe noted that any anxiety activates a physical response in a person's autonomic nervous system, creating a state of body tension. When the human body is subjected to continuous tension, it reacts like anything else under tension, such as a piece of wood or elastic. The part of the item subjected to the tension experiences some degree of physical breakdown. An aircraft, for example, is usually well maintained between flights. No matter how extensive the maintenance, though, the metal on the aircraft continually experiences stress as a result of air pressure. Eventually, the metal weakens from the pressure and becomes fatigued. Unless this fatigue is detected by the airline mechanics and corrected, the plane may collapse under the strain of flight. Blythe notes that airline companies practice a form of preventive medicine by constantly searching for metal fatigue and correcting such weaknesses as soon as they are found. The effects of air pressure on an aircraft closely parallel the effects of stress on a human being (Blythe, 1973).

## STRESS AS A CAUSE OF DISEASE AND ILLNESS

Blythe developed a list of ailments in which stress is viewed as a primary causal factor. This list was developed through interviews with experts in the field of medicine and a review of reports produced by the World Health Organization and the J. R. Geigy Pharmaceutical Company. The following illnesses have been identified as being closely associated with stress (Blythe, 1973):

Hypertension (high blood pressure)
Coronary thrombosis
Hay fever and other allergies
Migraine headaches
Intense itching
Asthma
Peptic ulcers
Constipation
Rheumatoid arthritis
Colitis
Menstrual difficulties
Nervous dyspepsia (flatulence and indigestion)
Overactive thyroid gland
Skin disorders
Diabetes mellitus
Tuberculosis

Selye (1976) describes numerous diseases associated with stress. He cites diseases of the kidney, heart, and blood vessels as being closely related to the degree of stress being experienced by an individual. He also indicts stress as a significant factor in causing and escalating inflammatory diseases such as arthritis and other rheumatic and rheumatoid diseases, inflammatory diseases of the skin and eyes, and allergies and hypersensistivity diseases. Diseases of the nervous system, sexual disorders, and metabolic diseases have as great a relationship to the amount of stress experienced by the individuals as they do to heredity and physical injury. Loss of weight and obesity, for example, are considered diseases of adaptation, that is, of how a person responds to his or her environment. Although conclusive evidence is still lacking, there appear to be direct links between stress and various forms of cancer. Selye, however, notes that the relationship between stress and cancer has been supported only to the point that additional research is necessary.

In their research on stress and physical disorders, Woolfolk and Richardson (1978) noted that stress reactions result from the interaction between a person and his or her environment. They cited four illnesses related to stress: hypertension, coronary disease, infections, and ulcers.

## Hypertension

Hypertension, or high blood pressure, develops over a period of time, often years, and produces few noticeable symptoms until it reaches its more advanced stages. Hypertension affects approximately one in every five American adults. Blood pressure increases during periods of stress, that is, whenever the person is aroused. Usually, when the arousal is brief, the blood pressure rises and then lowers to its normal state. When the stress is prolonged or intense, however, the rise in blood pressure may continue long after the source of stress has been eliminated. The high level of blood pressure may become permanent.

Hypertension has been cited as a major health problem among black Americans. Yet, a study of black residents living in middle-class neighborhoods had a rate of hypertension approximately one-half that found in black residents living in a ghetto environment. Another study revealed that black women living in rural areas of Mississippi had no greater frequency or rate of hypertension than white women living in the same or similar socioeconomic conditions. The ghetto-type environment, then, was cited as an etiologically significant factor in hypertension among its residents, who experience high levels of frustration from overcrowding, pollution, crime, and an unstable economic status.

Air traffic controllers are another group who experience an exceptionally high rate of hypertension. One study revealed that this occupational group experiences a hypertension rate approximately 5 times greater than comparable work groups. Stress in the field of air traffic control is associated with the amount of responsibility the individual controllers bear for the safety of others. Such psychologically demanding work apparently has a debilitating effect on those who perform it. This phenomenon is particularly important to human service practitioners who, like air traffic controllers, bear significant responsibility for the well-being of others and whose split-second decisions may have severe consequences.

## Coronary Disease

Although heart disease was relatively uncommon in the United States until the 1920s, it has become so widespread that more Americans die each year of heart attacks than of any other single cause. Recent studies have linked stress to heart disease along with the more generally accepted role of smoking, improper diet, lack of exercise, and heredity. Most heart attacks are attributable to arteriosclerosis, which occurs when fatty substances adhere to the walls of arteries. The fatty substances grow hard in time and cause the channel through which blood flows to narrow, reducing the flow of blood to the heart. When oxygen is cut off from the heart, the muscle tissue of the heart begins to die. The death of heart muscle tissue is known as myocardial infarction. In addition to myocardial infarction, the fatty substance on the artery walls may continue to grow until the supply of blood is completely cut off from the heart, or a piece of the substance may break away from the wall and flow into the heart where, being too large to pass, it blocks one of the coronary arteries.

The cause of arteriosclerosis, according to most researchers, is the fat level of the blood. Two of the fatty substances in the blood that are closely related to stress are cholesterol and triglycerides. Woolfolk and Richardson (1978) reported a study of race car drivers in which triglyceride levels in the blood were greatly elevated both before and during a race. Several hours after the race concluded, the triglyceride levels remained twice the normal level. This increase was attributed to the sudden stress to which the drivers were exposed. In studying tax accountants, it was noted that cholesterol levels rose as the April 15 tax date drew near. These levels did not decrease until almost 2 months later. In this situation, the cholesterol in the blood rose with the gradual but constant exposure to stress.

Research regarding personality factors and lifestyles as they relate to coronary disease was conducted by Friedman and Rosenman who identified coronary-prone individuals (Woolfolk and

Richardson, 1978). Their research led them to the conclusion that the coronary-prone person is not necessarily one who does not exercise or who has a bad diet. Rather, he or she is a person who is driven by ambition and a sense of urgency. This type of individual is generally aggressive, self-demanding, impatient, and always in a hurry. This individual, known as the Type-A personality, is constantly under stress.

The Type-B personality is less competitive, easy-going, and less hurried. He or she finds it easy to relax, is able to separate work from leisure time, and is less apt to become angry. He or she would not be considered impatient in any way. According to Friedman and Rosenman, the Type-A personality is 7 times more likely to develop coronary disease than the Type-B personality. Type-A individuals have higher levels of cholesterol and triglycerides in their blood. They also have greater fatty deposits and an excessive accumulation of insulin in their blood.

In addition to Type-A personality as potential for coronary disease, research has identified other factors, including frequent job changes and moving from a rural area to an urban area, as contributing factors. Living in a rural area that has changed or is changing to a more urbanized community is also a factor (Woolfolk and Richardson, 1978).

## Infectious Diseases

Much attention has recently been directed toward studying the relationship between stress and infectious illnesses. Woolfolk notes that people have long accepted the theory that tired, overworked people are susceptible to infections. A study was conducted of 24 women during a flu season. Some had very high concentrations of flu virus in their blood but did not become ill. Others who had very small amounts of the flu virus in their blood became ill. The women who had become ill, however, had undergone a recent and debilitating stressful experience. Holmes and Rahe further supported the relationship between stress and infectious illness. Using their inventory of 43 life events, the Social Readjustment Scale, they were able to predict an individual's susceptibility to illness with a high rate of success. A person scoring less than 150 total points on the Social Readjustment Scale was given a 37% probability of becoming ill within a 24-month period. Those scoring more than 150 but less than 300 were given a 51% chance of experiencing illness. A score in excess of 300 indicated that the individual had an 80% chance of developing illness within a 24-month period (Woolfolk and Richardson, 1978).

## Ulcers

Perhaps more than any other physical malady, ulcers tend to be associated with stress. Most people accept the stereotype of the active professional as one who works hard, expends a great deal of energy, and nurses an ulcer. Woolfolk and Richardson (1978) note that evidence relating psychological stress to disorders of the digestive system is conclusive. The most common disorder of the digestive system is the peptic ulcer, which occurs when digestive juices burn a hole in the lining of the stomach. Digestive juices are normally secreted whenever a person eats; they are also secreted when a person becomes highly emotional. Anger, for example, will stimulate rapid secretion of digestive juices or stomach acid (Woolfolk and Richardson, 1978). Selye (1976) states

> The gastrointestinal tract is particularly sensistive to general stress. Loss of appetite is one of the first symptoms in the great "syndrome of just being sick," and this may be accompanied by vomiting, diarrhea, or constipation. Signs of irritation and upset of the digestive organs may occur in any type of emotional stress. This is well known, not only to soldiers who experienced it during the tense expectation of battle, but even to students who pace the floor before my door, waiting ... for their turn in oral examinations.

It is also common knowledge that gastric and duodenal ulcers are most likely to occur in people who are somewhat maladjusted to their work or family life and suffer from constant tension and frustration (Selye, 1976).

The most revealing study of ulcers and their relationship to stress was conducted by Dr. Stewart Wolf. Because of an unusual injury to the esophagus of a patient, Dr. Wolf provided an opening in the stomach through which the injured person could be fed. For years, he was able to observe the patient's stomach functions on a regular basis. His observations showed that, when his patient responded to an emotional situation, excessive amounts of stomach acids were secreted. Other laboratory tests supported Wolf's findings that the amount of stomach acid increases when individuals are exposed to stress. When present in an empty stomach for prolonged periods of time, the acids begin to digest the stomach wall, causing an ulcer (Woolfolk and Richardson, 1978).

## ADAPTABILITY AND STRESS

The way in which an individual responds to stress physiologically is due, in part, to his or her ability to adapt. Much the same as Pavlov's dogs responded to a bell, a human being becomes conditioned to repeated stresses. The person who adapts well is less likely to suffer the negative effects of stress. For example, a person who lives in a home with a loudly ticking wall clock scarcely notices the sounds made by the clock. When guests visit, however, they may be disturbed by the noise of the clock. Reaction to the stresses of life are similar. A person may become seriously ill at the sight of blood when attempting to render aid at the scene of an automobile collision. This is clearly a reaction to stress. The person may also grow cold and shaky. For the police officer and paramedic, who have become somewhat conditioned to such situations, physical illness or nervousness usually does not occur.

## PSYCHOSOMATIC ILLNESS

Many people refer to illnesses related to stress as "psychosomatic," because no obvious physical cause such as injury exists for the symptoms that are present. Graham-Bonnalie (1972) believes that the ultimate difference between stress-induced illness and psychosomatic illness is one of terminology. In the generally accepted definition of psychosomatic illness, there are no structural physical changes present, although the symptoms exhibited by the sufferer suggest that there are. In physical illnesses attributed to stress, the popular thought is that structural physical changes have, in fact, occurred.

It is clear that the relationship between mind and body exists. An individual involved in an unhappy marriage may develop peptic ulcers, and the employee who is constantly reprimanded by a supervisor may develop allergies. In both cases, the illnesses reflect a physical change occurring as a result of either a mental or emotional process. Several studies on abdominal illnesses of children have demonstrated that reaction to stress through physical illness begins at a young age and follows through the adult years (Graham-Bonnalie, 1972).

Graham-Bonnalie speaks of a variety of illnesses that may be induced by exposure to stress. Among these illnesses are:

Acne
Alcoholism
Allergies
Alopecia areata (a condition in which relatively large patches of
    hair fall out within a short period of time)
Anorexia nervosa ("starvation" dieting or undereating to the
    point of emaciation)
Appendicitis
Asthma
Cancer
Colitis
Constipation
Dermatitis and eczema
Diabetes
Diarrhea
Enureris (bedwetting)
Eye conditions
Fatigue
Frigidity
Gout
Headache and migraine
Heart conditions, including hypertension
Impotence

Insomnia
Obesity
Peptic ulcers
Psoriasis
Rheumatic fever
Rheumatoid arthritis

Such psychosomatic illnesses become "escape routes" for coping with stress.

## SUMMARY

Clearly, there is ample support for the hypothesis that a correlation exists between stress and illness; new studies conducted by government, colleges and universities, and private sources are confirming this correlation. Researchers continue to dispute the extent to which this relationship exists; however, few dispute its existence. The study of Holmes and Rahe (1976) predicted potential for illness with uncanny accuracy. The nature of an individual's personality was clearly tied to susceptibility to illness. Woolfolk and Richardson (1978) state that, "Even if one is very conservative in evaluating the available evidence, the list of physical maladies in which stress probably plays a role is quite long. Migraine headaches, backaches, asthma, constipation, acute dermatitis, menstrual pain, colitis, diarrhea, diabetes, arthritis, and even cancer have been linked to stress. It is clear that stress is a serious problem, which we have a considerable stake in combating." Since the recognition of stress as a major factor plaguing people's well-being is a recent phenomenon, many more years of study are required before conclusive statements may be made on the degree to which stress causes physical illness.

# Chapter 4
# Identifying the Symptoms of Stress

Over a period of time, exposure to negative stress takes its toll on an individual's physical, mental, and emotional well-being. Industries and businesses throughout the world have recognized the impact of constant, daily exposure to negative stress on employee performance. They have implemented a wide variety of health and benefit programs to assist employees in recognizing and coping with the negative effects of stress.

In most human service fields, the number of programs designed to aid practitioners in identifying and coping with stress is small. Although some hospitals offer mental health programs to physicians and nurses and some police agencies provide stress management training to officers, probation officers, classroom teachers, and social workers have few, if any, stress reduction programs made available to them by their agencies. Physicians and dentists who are self-employed have no agency to provide such programs, although occasional workshops and seminars on stress management are offered by professional organizations and associations. In almost all of the human service fields, primary responsibility for the recognition and resolution of negative stress and its effects rests with the individual practitioner. Since negative effects of stress most often express themselves in disturbances of physical and mental functioning, the practitioner, if he or she is to prove effective

65

in identifying its symptoms, must have a basic understanding of physical and mental health and well-being.

## WHAT IS HEALTH?

For most people, physical health is the absence of illness. Although simplistic, this definition has been accepted for generations by the medical profession and the general public. More recently, many people have begun to think of physical health as a state of "wellness," epitomized in a lifestyle that is based on sound diet, regular exercise, and preventive health care. Physical health is thus characterized by participation in a pro-active effort, i.e., an energetic approach toward prevention of illness, to ensure vitality and well-being, as well as by the absence of illness.

People measure physical health in different ways. For some, an absence of colds during a particularly hard winter is a sign of good health. A good dental check-up may be viewed as a measure of health by others. For still others, demonstrating strength by lifting a large amount of weight or being able to jog two miles a day may constitute good health.

People have a different concept of mental health and well-being. They do not, as a rule, view mental health as the simple absence of mental illness. Many people do not acknowledge the existence of mental illness. They give little or no thought to mental "wellness." Taking a pro-active approach to ensuring mental health is a relatively new concept in modern society.

Most people do not possess the knowledge, skill, or desire to measure their mental well-being. They do not recognize the symptoms of mental illness in themselves or when exhibited in others. The symptoms are often vague, unlike those in physical illness. When symptoms are recognized, they are often denied because of the stereotyped image of mentally ill persons that is prevalent in today's society.

A mentally healthy person is a well-adjusted person. He or she is not unduly distressed by daily conflicts. Problems are dealt with in a realistic manner, the inevitable is accepted with little difficulty, and personal shortcomings and the shortcomings of others are understood and accepted, and are not viewed negatively. By contrast, a maladjusted individual is unduly disturbed by daily conflicts. He or she often denies reality in attempting to resolve these conflicts and in dealing with people and problems (Hilgard, 1953).

Jahoda (1958) links mental health with the possession of certain traits or dimensions of behavior. He has indicated that a mentally healthy individual has:

A realistic understanding of himself
The ability to become mature and to learn by experience
An integrated personality
Sufficient independence to enable himself to make decisions and act on them
A realistic perception of his social environment
The ability to control himself and, to some extent, his environment

## REACTIONS TO STRESS

People react to stress in many ways. They may exert extra energy to accomplish a task, laugh, cry, boast, curse, or day-dream. Each of these reactions is intended to reduce tension. When tension is not reduced through one of these actions, stress continues to mount. A report by the International Association of Chiefs of Police (IACP) notes that an individual who cannot reduce stress through simple means may become tense and exhibit excessive nervousness and worry. He or she may also experience minor bodily dysfunctions. If the conflicts causing the tension are quickly resolved, these reactions rapidly disappear (IACP, 1978).

When the tension is not relieved, increased discomfort, anxiety, and feelings of uselessness may be experienced. Feelings of guilt and fear also increase. The individual's ability to work may decline and he or she may experience difficulty in getting along with others. The IACP identifies three specific reactions to stress: repression of emotion, displacement of anger, and isolation. Although intended to show the reactions of police personnel to stress, these specific stress reactions are experienced by most human service professionals.

## Repression of Emotion

From the time they enter their jobs until the time they resign or retire, human service professionals are generally taught to avoid showing their emotions when dealing with clients, patients, or students. They are told to remain impartial and objective and to avoid showing signs of fear, sadness, anger, disgust, or weakness. They learn to repress these emotions in order to effectively meet the needs of those they serve.

In time, most human service workers suppress their emotional responsiveness as well as their emotional expression. The exhibition of emotion is strongly inhibited. The more frequently a practitioner is exposed to situations that are emotionally charged, the stronger his or her defenses become against feeling the emotions and exhibiting outward expressions of them. Eventually, the practitioner may not be able to relax these defenses and may appear emotionless and objective even when interacting with family and friends. Although it appears that the individual is void of emotional feelings, these feelings are simply masked and held inside, and may ultimately result in mental and emotional disorders.

## Displacement of Anger

Most human service practitioners are given their daily assignments or duties by others. Teachers cannot hand-pick their students, and physicians cannot select their patients from a list of people needing treatment. Specific instructions are given to many practitioners on how to plan, perform, and evaluate their activities. Policies, procedures, and directives are issued in abundance. Although the practitioner may be concerned about a particular directive or policy or may be angry about the way in which services are being provided to clients, there typically are few channels available to express and clarify his or her views.

Since feelings, beliefs, opinions, attitudes, and values cannot always be expressed while on the job, frustration mounts.

In order to cope with this frustration, the practitioner may release his or her anger at colleagues and clients on the job and toward family members and friends after work. Sudden outbursts of anger or hostility are a common symptom of stress.

## Isolation

Human service practitioners are not always readily welcomed, even when their services are patently helpful. People may be uncomfortable with having to accept welfare funds. Many people are traumatized when they have to visit a dentist or physician. Most people are uncomfortable interacting with the police, regardless of the nature of the situation. Even being questioned as a witness may be highly threatening. Many students dislike school.

A common result of the public's distrust and rejection is a sense of isolation on the part of the caregiver. The practitioner who feels isolated and alienated may only be able to express his or her feelings when in the company of selected peers or family members. In other cases, even family members are resented for not understanding the role and problems of the practitioner. The practitioner begins to seek and attend to information and perspectives only from others in his or her field, and purposefully avoids people who are not in the human service fields. Such withdrawal from most or all human contact and communication is characteristic of profound human loneliness and isolation. Becoming isolated in this way is a trait common to a person experiencing stress (IACP, 1978).

## RECOGNIZING THE SYMPTOMS OF STRESS

Understanding the traits that characterize good physical and mental health can assist an individual in identifying the symptoms of stress. With such understanding, many of the symptoms are obvious. Others are subtle and require monitoring over a period of time or professional consultation.

For the human service practitioner, as for most people, one of the most effective ways to identify the symptoms of stress is to make regular preventive visits to a family physician, a specialist physician, and a dentist. These professionals are more likely to detect warning signs of stress than the individual himself or herself. A dentist, for example, can identify signs of tooth grinding, a trait common to people experiencing extreme or severe stress. Tooth grinding may occur at night while an individual sleeps. It can be recognized by qualified professionals through observation of the wear patterns of teeth, broken fillings, and fractured teeth. Current dental research and treatment programs recognize tooth grinding as a high predictor of patient stress (Kinzer, 1979). Similarly, a family physician, after conducting tests on possible physical causes, may identify a person's back pains as psychosomatic, that is, brought about by mental or emotional strain.

**Warning Signs**

The most common symptoms of stress can be easily recognized, and warn the individual that his or her body, mind, and emotions are not reacting positively to the strains and tensions of life. When under stress, an individual may experience a variety of malfunctions within the vulnerable parts of the body. These serve as warning signs or symptoms of negative stress. One person may experience severe headaches, and another may have trouble sleeping. Both people may be responding to the cumulative effects of stress at home and/or at work. Selye (1976) has explored warning signs that may be exhibited when people are under stress. The following list of signs represents his thinking and that of many other professionals working in the field of stress.

General irritability, hyperexcitation, or depression
Dryness of the throat and mouth
Impulsive behavior, emotional instability
Inability to concentrate, general disorientation
Feelings of weakness, dizziness, loss of reality
Fatigue
Floating anxiety, irrational fears

Emotional tension, sense of being "keyed up"
Trembling, nervous tics
Tendency to be easily startled
Nervous, generally high-pitched laughter
Stuttering and other speech difficulties
Tooth grinding
Insomnia
Sweating
Frequent urination
Diarrhea, indigestion, stomach ailments, vomiting
Migraine headaches
Premenstrual tension, abnormal menstrual cycles
Lower back pain, neck pain, chest pain
Loss of appetite, compulsive eating
Excessive smoking, increased smoking
Increased use of prescribed drugs
Alcohol dependency, drug addiction
Nightmares
Neurotic behavior
Psychoses
Accident-prone behavior

Because stress affects people in so many ways, physically, mentally, and emotionally, there are a wide variety of symptoms to be considered. Tresidder (1977) has divided the symptoms into physical signs and mental signs. This division is an effective way of categorizing the typical signs of stress.

### Physical Signs

Excess weight, with consideration of height and age
High blood pressure
Lack of appetite
Impulsive eating at the first sign of a problem
Frequent heartburn
Chronic diarrhea or constipation
Loss of sleep
Constant fatigue

Daily need for medication such as aspirin
Frequent headaches
Muscle spasms
Sense of "fullness" without having eaten
Shortness of breath
Tendency toward fainting or nausea
Tendency toward sudden outbursts of tears or an inability to cry
Frigidity, impotence
Excessive nervous energy

### Mental Signs

Constant feeling of uneasiness
Irritability toward family and associates at work
General sense of boredom
Recurring feelings of hopelessness in coping with life
Anxiety about money
Irrational fear of disease
Fear of death
Feelings of suppressed anger
Inability to laugh easily and openly
Feelings of rejection by family members
Feelings of despair at failing as a parent
Feelings of dread toward an approaching weekend
Reluctance to vacation
Sense that problems cannot be discussed with others
Inability to concentrate or to complete one task before beginning
     another
Fear of heights, enclosed places, thunderstorms, or earthquakes

The Holmes and Rahe (1967) scale of life events provides another technique for identifying the impact of negative stress. For example, a person who has recently reconciled a marriage and changed jobs within the same period of time is under significant stress, even though both events may be very positive. Regardless of the positive or negative nature of the events, a high score on the scale indicates that a person may be prone to the physical, mental, and emotional problems associated with stress. A person with a high score should avoid engaging in additional high-stress activities until some of the present stress is relieved. A person scoring low on the scale may be able to engage in additional stress-producing activities with little or no long-term harmful effects.

In dealing with stress, people should avoid overreacting when they identify several of the warning signs in themselves. Instead, the identified symptoms should serve as cautionary signs that potential danger exists. As with any other warning signs, *appropriate* action should be taken. Chapter 5 presents some of the alternatives and solutions available to cope with stress.

# Chapter 5
# Coping with and Reducing Stress: A Personal Approach

Yates (1979) notes that people sometimes need an increased amount of stress when their lives begin to appear flat or sterile. At other times, when stress has become excessive, they need to take action to reduce it. In the human service fields, as in many professions, practitioners may create stress in others to generate a specific activity or to increase someone's productivity. For example, a supervisor may warn an employee whose performance has faltered. Practitioners may also assist others in reducing the stress that is causing them to be ineffective or unproductive. In each of these situations, an individual assumes responsibility for controlling the degree and nature of stress in others.

The techniques an individual may employ in managing stress are many and varied. Numerous self-help texts have been written to assist people in controlling anxiety and tension, relaxing, ensuring mental health, and improving self-esteem. Courses for college credit, workshops, and seminars that focus on stress reduction techniques are offered in most communities.

Selye states that the first step toward coping with and reducing stress is to "know thyself and be thyself" (Selye, 1976). He adds, however, that this is one of the most difficult things for a person to do. Because human service practitioners must, to a great extent, keep their emotions to themselves, they tend to wear "masks" that hide and distort their real personalities. If they deny their emotions in service to others, they cannot possibly be themselves. The problem is exacerbated when the practitioner's true feelings are not as humanistic as he or she thinks they should be. He or she is psychologically distorted in the process of conforming to this idealized humanitarian role. Being a continuous doer of good can lead to self-denigration, and paradoxically, to the denigration of clients, patients, and students. Selye repeats the advice of Matthew Arnold:

> Resolve to be thyself: and know that he
> Who finds himself, loses his misery.

Knowing oneself, one's attitudes, values, and innermost feelings, is a critical first step in knowing others. Particularly important is becoming aware, as much as possible, of subconscious feelings and repressed experiences. Subconscious conflicts may be manifesting themselves in mental and physical problems and disorders. Once most people intellectually and emotionally understand the source of the conflict, the impact of the disorders subsides, unless the emotional effect of stress has resulted in irreversable physical damage. The process of eliminating many of the masks that are worn will result in reduced stress.

Similarly, it is important that an individual become aware of his or her body and physical capabilities and limitations. Many human service professionals work long, tiring hours to provide service to clients. They often refuse to recognize their physical limitations. Insufficient time is given to relaxation, sleep, and eating properly. Many human service practitioners maintain an unrealistic attitude toward their physical capabilities and needs, much the same as a middle-age, out-of-condition man who attempts to play tackle football with neighborhood high school students. At some point, the body responds to this form of physical stress, usually in a negative way. Selye (1976) believes that a person who hopes to cope with and reduce the harmful effects of stress must first "dissect" his or her current state of being. Once this is done, the individual will be able to determine whether or not he or she wants to participate in specific stress reduction techniques and programs.

In determining the degree of stress to which an individual is exposed, the Holmes and Rahe "Social Readjustment Rating Scale," discussed in Chapter 1, may be used. In addition, the symptoms cited in Chapter 4 should be reviewed. Because the way in which a person responds to stress is individual, there can be no established structured pattern that is universally applicable. As usual, no ready panacea is available. Each practitioner will have to establish the stress reduction and control program that best meets his or her needs.

The ideal way to reduce the negative effects of stress is to eliminate the cause of the stress. For most people, particularly for those working in the human service fields, this is generally impossible. The stress caused by increased demands for service, exposure to human grief, and other elements common to the human service professions cannot be eliminated. *The best technique, then, for coping with and reducing stress is gaining the physical and inner strength necessary to deal with it more effectively and participating in activities that lessen its impact on the body, mind, and spirit.*

## EXERCISE AS A STRESS REDUCTION TECHNIQUE

Physical exercise has been recognized as an effective tool in reducing and coping with stress. Its benefits are many. In addition to stimulating the body, exercise strengthens the cardiovascular system and causes most people to relax when they have finished their routine. In explaining the rapidly increasing incidence of hypertension, heart attack, and stroke in the United States, Benson (1975) cites lack of exercise as one of the three primary causes. Lack of exercise is also a cause of boredom, which may lead to job dissatisfaction and cause stress (Pembrook, 1978).

Numerous studies have shown that a relationship exists between improved physical fitness and a reduction in anxiety and

depression. In one study, conducted by Dr. H. A. DeVries, decreased electrical activity, i.e., excitability, in the muscles was
noted in people who improved their physical fitness. This decrease represented a reduction in tension, restlessness, and
anxiety (DeRosis, 1979).

Using Selye's definition of stress as the physiological response of the body to any demand placed on it, exercise may be
viewed as a source of stress. Yates confirms that exercise is a
stressful activity that is useful in combating the ravages of stress
or distress. However, if a person exercises to extremes, the exercise also becomes harmful and causes distress (Yates, 1979).
Therefore, anyone pursuing an exercise program as a way in
which to reduce stress should be conscious of his or her physical
limitations. The dangers associated with some exercises should
also be considered. For example, there is a high risk of accidents
in jogging and bicycling as a result of falls and vehicular colli-
sions. In undertaking any exercise program that represents a
drastic change in physical activity, individuals should first consult a physician.

In addition to contacting a physician prior to beginning an
exercise program, a number of other precautions should be
taken. Observing these precautions should prevent the positive
process of exercising from becoming a source of distress.

1. Exercise should be undertaken gradually. Too many people
   attempt to gain overnight results, leading to complications,
   and thus the exercise causes more problems than it resolves.
2. Prior to participating in an exercise routine, warm-up activities should be conducted. These may include a few minutes
   of stretching exercises or other activities that prepare the
   body to cope with the rigor of exercise.
3. A person participating in an exercise program should be
   alert and respond to physiological warning signs. Dizziness,
   nausea, feelings of exhaustion, breathlessness, and pains in
   the muscles or chest are signs of overexertion.
4. Exercise should be undertaken on a regularly scheduled
   basis, at least three or four times each week. Vigorous exer-

cise undertaken only occasionally or on weekends is often more harmful than not participating in any physical activity. A regular routine should be established and, whenever possible, adhered to.

5. A period of time should be allotted following an exercise program for "cooling down." This is as important as the warm-up period and should last for at least 5 minutes.

6. A person participating in an exercise program should drink a larger volume of liquid per day than was consumed prior to beginning the program.

7. Heavy meals should be avoided before exercising. If a heavy meal is consumed, a period of approximately 2 hours should be allotted prior to exercising.

8. Exercise should be avoided completely during periods of illness.

9. Proper equipment should be worn for the specific exercises being done. A good pair of jogging shoes, for example, will prevent many of the injuries normally associated with running.

10. A person engaging in an exercise program should learn to monitor his or her pulse. If the beat of the heart does not return to within 10 beats of normal 15 minutes after exercising, then the individual has overexerted himself or herself. The amount, intensity, or duration of exercise should be reduced the next time it is attempted.

A regular exercise program following the precautions listed above will result in an improved ability to withstand stress. Studies at the University of California, under the direction of Dr. Ernest Michael, support the biological principle that action absorbs anxiety. In one study, he tested two groups of people: one group participated in a regular exercise program and the other did not. Each group was subjected to conditions designed to induce stress. The group that participated in the exercise program demonstrated a greater ability to adjust to stress and to recover from its effects. The most effective exercises used were walking and swimming. These activities are rhythmic and make use of many muscles. Michael noted, "The studies showed that regular exercise not only increases nervous stamina appreciably, but serves another equally valuable purpose: it provides an effective means for the discharge and release of nervous and emotional tensions. Unless these tensions are discharged, pressures on the nerves continue to multiply" (Galton, 1979).

The benefits of physical exercise go beyond coping with mental and emotional tension. Exercise aids in maintaining weight at a desirable level, another significant factor in coping with and reducing stress. Exercise alters the basic composition of body tissue by increasing the proportion of muscle and decreasing the proportion of fat. Muscles that may not have been used for a long period of time become toned and stronger. Endurance and strength are increased. Coordination and flexibility of joints are increased, often reducing minor aches and pains that occur in these areas. Feelings of listlessness and fatigue may diminish and general appearance improves (Galton, 1979).

The types of exercise should suit the individual tastes and needs of each person. There is no single exercise program suited to all people. A person who hates the idea of jogging every other morning can find other exercises that will provide the same physiological effects. A person who does not have access to a swimming pool should not be discouraged, even though swimming is frequently cited as one of the best possible exercises.

Since stress is so closely related to the functions of the cardiovascular system, those exercises that strengthen the heart and increase the circulation should be assigned first priority in any exercise program. It is important to focus on aerobic exercises in a fitness program. Aerobics require the body to utilize as much oxygen as possible. A person who lifts weights or does stretching exercises in a gradual manner will benefit from improved muscle tone. However, these exercises and others of the isometric type do little to improve the cardiovascular system. Jogging, bicycle riding, brisk walking, and swimming are a few of the aerobic exercises that strengthen the cardiovascular system. Others include those sports or activities that involve repeated, continuous movement such as handball, soccer, hiking, basketball, racquetball, rowing, skipping rope, and cross-country skiing. An energetic program of calisthenics may also be helpful in strengthening the heart. In all of these exercises and activities, motion is both continuous and rhythmic and places some strain on the body.

Katch, McArdle, and Boylan (1979) note that improved fitness does not occur haphazardly. For physiological improvements to occur, there must be a regular program of activity in which the body experiences some amount of overload or physiological stress. When this occurs, a person is asking more from his or her body than is usually required and the body responds. An effective exercise program is based on the proper application of overload or physiological stress. A person who begins a program for the first time should start at an overload level just slightly above normal. Overload can be accomplished in several ways. First, the *frequency* of exercise may be increased. Second, the *intensity* of the exercise within a specific time period may be increased. Third, the *duration* of the exercise at a specified intensity may be increased (Katch, McArdle, and Boylan, 1979).

A physician who decides to pursue jogging to improve her cardiovascular system may decide to jog four or five blocks every third day for 1 year. To be more effective and to gain more benefits, she should consider one of the three methods of overload. She could increase the speed of running, which would expand the intensity of the exercise. She could also increase the distance run or the number of days or frequency of participation. To ensure continued improvement, she must adjust to the changes caused by the exercise, physiologically and in performance level (Katch, McArdle, and Boylan, 1979).

Few human service practitioners work an established time schedule. Irregular hours and long periods of overtime are the norm in many of the helping professions. Irregular hours interfere with scheduling and implementation of an exercise program conducted at regular intervals during the week. By following two basic guidelines, a systematic exercise program may be implemented despite irregular work hours. Most physiologists and physical development experts believe that a person should participate in an exercise program at least three times each week. No more than 2 days should be allowed between activities or periods of exercise. The exercise period should last for 30 to 50 minutes, including 5 to 10 minutes for warming up and 5 to 10 minutes for cooling down. Most human service workers should be able to fit a 30–50 minute period of exercise into their routine three times each week.

Detailed information on specific exercise programs may be found in libraries, book stores, many magazines, and in literature provided by local, state, and federal governments. In addition to specific exercise programs, human service practitioners can participate in a variety of exercises while on the job. For example, they can increase the amount of energy expended during the time allotted to normal, daily routines. Katch refers to this exercise technique as a form of exercise behavior modification known as substituting alternate behavior. Some of the activities to be considered are:

1. For those people who work in an office, parking approximately one-half mile away from work and briskly walking the remaining distance will burn up the caloric equivalent of seven pounds of fat in 1 year.
2. People using public transportation should consider getting off several blocks before their usual stop and walking the remaining distance.
3. In traveling short distances, people should walk rather than use a car or public transportation.
4. Time allotted to coffee breaks during the work day could be spent doing simple exercises in place.
5. Some people may prefer to wake up earlier than usual to take a brisk walk, jog, or ride a bicycle. Again, the dangers of jogging and bicycling should be considered prior to participating in either exercise activity.
6. Exercise should be included as part of weekly family outings or recreational activities. Activities may include participa-

tion in sports or may simply involve parking several blocks from a destination and walking the remaining distance.

7. Simple exercises may be done during television commercials or during other leisure periods at home. These may include running in place, cycling on an exercise bicycle, or walking up and down stairs several times.

8. People working in multistory buildings should use stairs instead of elevators.

9. When possible, several people may get together to form simple exercise groups that meet before or after work or during lunch periods.

10. For those people who live within a reasonable distance of their office and who do not require a car to perform their daily function, a bicycle may be used to travel to and from work. Vehicular traffic flow should be considered first.

There are many other daily activities that may be approached as opportunities for physical exercise. Mowing a lawn, washing a car, walking a dog, and painting all require some degree of overload. It is important, however, that physical activity be approached systematically and that competing leisure time and work pursuits not interfere with regular participation in some sort of exercise (Katch, McArdle, and Boylan, 1979).

## DIET AND NUTRITION IN
## STRESS REDUCTION AND CONTROL

One of the primary excuses given for their poor eating habits by people who are hurried, burdened with work, or consumed by their daily activities is that they do not have sufficient time to attend to proper nutrition. They justify their dietary habits with a variety of reasons:

1. They do not have the time to prepare meals.

2. They try to eat at least one good meal each day, and depend on snacks and fast foods to provide nutrients during the remainder of the day.

3. They get their meals while out, generally at fast food restaurants.
4. They are unable to plan their meals because of time and budgetary constraints.

These people also eat while engaged in other activities, such as reading or watching television. They eat almost unconsciously, paying little or no attention to what they are consuming.

Many human service practitioners are poor eaters. In their haste during a busy workday they skip breakfast, grab a cup of coffee while on the move, eat a quick lunch from a fast-food counter, and hurry through dinner in order to get to the paperwork that has to be completed before returning to the office in the morning. Even those practitioners who put a great deal of emphasis on physical exercise will often consume the wrong foods in a hurried manner.

Such poor eating habits eventually take their toll. Poor diet can result in chronic anxiety, trembling, dizziness, weakness, fatigue, depression, and excessive weight. In some cases, such as hypoglycemia (low blood sugar), symptoms may include convulsions and loss of consciousness.

The precise relationship between diet and stress remains unclear; however, most physicians and researchers agree that the relationship exists. In some specific situations, such as obesity and high or low blood sugar, the relationship is clear. The person who goes for a long period of time without eating a substantial and well-balanced meal will become tired and irritable. If he or she eats a candy bar or cupcake, a sudden surge of energy will occur as the body's blood sugar level is raised. Once this sugar is absorbed, however, a letdown will occur and the person once again becomes tired and irritable. The diet-stress relationship is more graphic when considering people with weight problems. They must function in a society that places a great deal of emphasis on being thin and socially penalizes those who are significantly overweight.

## Obesity and Dieting

Obesity is a diet-related illness that is often referred to as a stress disease (McQuade and Aikman, 1974). Obesity creates a mental stress since the obese individual is considered unattractive by society's standards. Overweight individuals must deal with their own feelings and the feelings of others toward their physical appearance. Also, the additional weight is a direct cause of physical stress. Their bodies must work harder to perform daily tasks such as climbing steps, walking, carrying objects, or performing simple housework. This additional strain on the body often makes a person vulnerable to other serious ailments such as diabetes, kidney disease, hypertension, and heart trouble.

In addition to causing stress, obesity is often caused by stress. Many people rely on food as a means for coping with or masking tensions, anxieties, and fears. Dieting is more difficult for them than for persons who are not nervous eaters and are therefore not dependent on food for relief from stress.

For people who are overweight, dieting to achieve a balance between weight and height and to gain a feeling of physical comfort and well-being is an effective means of reducing stress. However, dieting is a complex matter. Fad diets and dietary aids are most often ineffective in generating a long-term weight loss, particularly for people who are nervous eaters. They do little to modify an individual's behavior toward food, which is a key to successful long-term weight loss.

Before taking any action toward dramatically changing dietary habits, whether it be to lose weight or to reduce cholesterol, an individual should contact his or her physician. For most people in good health, the best way to maintain a healthy body weight while ensuring the intake of essential nutrients is to eat a balanced diet, focusing on the four food groups. Between-meal snacks that are high in sugar, salt, and caffein content should be assiduously avoided. For the average person to lose weight, a simple reduction in the volume of food eaten, i.e., the total number of calories consumed, should be sufficient.

The average American, for example, consumes approximately 3000 calories each day, but can live quite comfortably on 2600. The reduction in calories, particularly when accompanied by moderate or vigorous exercise, will usually result in weight loss (McQuade and Aikman, 1974). When attempting to lose weight, a person should focus on the loss of only 2 to 5 pounds each month. Weight loss, to be safe, should be gradual and regular over a long period of time (McQuade and Aikman, 1974).

## Good Nutrition

Most American diets consist of a large volume of fats. Yates notes that about 40% of the average American's intake of calories comes from fats (Yates, 1979). He adds that the average citizen has a count of about 200 milligrams of cholesterol (a dietary fat) for each 100 cubic centimeters of blood. Frederick Stare, a Harvard nutritionist, warns that cholesterol levels are dangerous when they reach 230 milligrams. Most Americans, therefore, are in danger of having too much cholesterol in their blood (Yates, 1979).

Americans also consume a large volume of salt, sugar, and caffeine, all of which are harmful to a person's physical health and, ultimately, to the way in which he or she responds to stress. Consuming simple sugars, such as those found in honey and refined white sugar, in too great a volume, increases the triglyceride count in the blood to unsafe proportions. Triglycerides, like cholesterol, are associated with risk factors in heart disease. Those people who consume large volumes of coffee and eat convenience foods and fast foods are ingesting significant amounts of cholesterol, salt, caffeine, and sugar.

The best possible diet for a person who is in sound health is one that is nutritionally balanced and includes cholesterol and other fats, sugars, and salt in small amounts. The basic food groups provide a foundation on which to build individual dietary habits. They are the milk group, the meat group, the bread and cereal group, and the fruit and vegetable group. For adults, it is recommended that two or more servings each day come from the milk and meat groups and that four or more servings per day come from the fruit and vegetable and bread and cereal groups.

The milk group includes all forms of dairy products, including cheese, yogurt, and ice cream. It is a main source of calcium for the body and provides protein, riboflavin, and other nutrients. The meat group includes beef, pork, veal, lamb, organ meats, poultry, eggs, fish, shellfish, dried beans, and nuts. These foods are a primary source of protein and provide other nutrients to the body, such as iron and niacin.

The vegetable and fruit group contains green and yellow vegetables and citrus fruits, tomatoes, and other fruits. It also contains such foods as potatoes, corn, and lima beans. This group is a major source of vitamins and minerals in a person's diet. The bread and cereal group contains pasta, rice, corn meal, flour, and breads and cereals. These foods provide carbohydrates, iron, vitamins, and complex sugars to the diet.

For human service practitioners who, because of their work routine, cannot eat three balanced meals each day, vitamin and mineral supplements will provide some of the nutrients missing from their diets. People with such a work routine, however, should consider changing or modifying their priorities to allow time for three balanced meals. Vitamin and mineral supplements combined with a program of weight control and a balanced diet will enhance a person's physical well-being. Physical health, in turn, will enable the individual to withstand the physical and mental effects of stress more effectively.

## MAINTAINING GOOD MENTAL HEALTH PRACTICES TO REDUCE AND COPE WITH STRESS

Sound mental health practices are as important to coping with and reducing stress as are good physical health practices. Yates notes, "A strong psychological adjustment on the part of an individual is known to effectively help offset the dysfunctional effects of stress" (Yates, 1979). He adds that the Shaffer and Shoben list of conditions for good mental health provides a representative sampling of techniques to be used. The following list describes some of these techniques.

1. Maintain good physical health to increase resistance against stressors that affect the mind and the body. The relationship between a healthy body and healthy mind has been recognized by the medical profession. It has been estimated, for example, that approximately 50% of all illness is psychosomatic in origin (Yates, 1979).
2. Self-acceptance is a major step toward sound mental health. A person who is aware of his or her strengths, weaknesses, failures, and successes maintains a realistic self-concept and is able to avoid many of the personal and interpersonal behaviors that create a stressful work environment. Self-acceptance is a difficult task that requires continuous, life-long evaluation. A realistic attitude toward one's self and one's abilities and limitations is an effective defense against negative effects of stress.
3. Yates notes that maintaining a confidante, someone in whom a person can confide and trust, is another stress reduction and prevention technique. This person may be a spouse, sibling, parent, coworker, neighbor, or friend.
4. Good mental health can be maintained and stress reduced through regular interaction with people who do not work in the same organization or field. Selye notes that it may be harmful to associate professionally and socially *only* with coworkers (Selye, 1976). Because many human service workers share the same stresses, concerns, and work hours, particularly those who work varying shifts, it is not uncommon to have a work group also function as a social group. Conversation at social functions then revolves around the problems and concerns of the work environment. A problem develops when the work group becomes the exclusive social group, since this allows little opportunity for complete relaxation from the stress associated with the job.
5. Involvement in a creative experience is another way to ensure good mental health. This involves participation in an

activity, either on the job or at home, that is unrelated to the normal routine. These activities may include hobbies, exercise programs, gardening and yard work, or any task that offers a challenge to the normal mental processes. They may be relaxing, stimulating, vigorous, or refreshing. A person who engages in such creative experiences should do so at regular intervals each week, preferably several times weekly.

6. Selye (1976) states that an individual who enjoys his or her work will have the greatest potential for reducing and coping with stress. Being comfortable in and enthusiastic toward the work environment is also conducive to good mental health. Yates (1979) warns against leaving a good work environment, in which an individual is happy, for the sake of additional salary. The negative effects of stress in an unhealthy work environment will ultimately have more impact on the well-being of an individual than the lack of additional income.

7. Use of the scientific method in personal problem solving is effective in maintaining sound mental health. Most professionals in the human service fields apply this method to solving the problems and concerns of their clients, patients, and students. It involves analyzing a situation, determining the precise problem to be resolved, studying the alternatives available for solving it, and taking the appropriate solution. Applying this technique to personal problems is sometimes difficult because of the highly personal nature of human concerns. However, it is applicable to many of the life problems that cause stress. By studying a personal problem or concern as objectively as possible and exploring as many alternatives as possible to address it, the opportunity for resolution increases.

There are many other techniques available to people to assist them in maintaining good mental health. Winter states, "You can overcome tension and achieve relaxation using the power of your mind alone." There are available techniques, she adds, that "involve no magic, nor do they require special skills;

indeed, almost anyone can employ them" (Winter, 1976). The techniques Winter refers to include biofeedback, transcendental meditation, hypnosis, and behavior modification. For the human service practitioner who regularly deals with highly stressful and emotional situations, application of one or more of these techniques may provide an effective means for avoiding the negative effects of stress.

## Biofeedback

Biofeedback is a process that enables a person to control or manipulate various bodily functions that were previously believed to be not consciously controllable. The process employs basic conditioning techniques to teach people to lower their blood pressure or to change their heart rate or body temperature by means of mental signals. Electronic devices are used at first to show the individual whether he or she has achieved change in a bodily function. In time, these devices are no longer needed.

Dr. Neal Miller confirmed the direct link between the mind and involuntary functions of the body. He experimented with patients in artificial lungs who could not control their own respiration and with victims of muscular dystrophy who could not tense their muscles. After learning biofeedback techniques, both groups of patients were able to lower their blood pressure through voluntary mental control. Miller noted that learning biofeedback is a trial and error process, similar to most learning situations. He demonstrated that rabbits and other animals could be taught to control their blood pressure, given the appropriate training and rewards (Winter, 1976).

Dr. Elmer Green studied a yogi who had been trained in the Himalayan mountains. With use of the electronic equipment, Green found that the yogi could change the temperature in his hand so that the side closest to the thumb varied 10 degrees from the side closest to the little finger. The yogi was also able to stop his heart from pumping blood and could induce specific brainwave patterns on request. These abilities were the result of a lifestyle and philosophy different from those of most people; however, the control of involuntary bodily functions through the mental process was confirmed (Winter, 1976).

Various skills are taught in biofeedback. The individual learns to relax the muscles that affect his or her involuntary functions and to recognize how this process feels. This is accomplished by observing the visible signs of these functions. For example, the activity of the brain may be measured by an electroencephalograph, the activities of the heart by an electrocardiograph, and the activity of the muscles by an electromyograph. Reactions of the skin may also be measured through use of a dermohmeter. The process of self-mastery is viewed on the screens or scopes of the equipment or is recognized through sounds that are made when an individual tenses his or her muscles while wired to the devices. In time, the control of the muscles is accomplished without use of electronic aids. Body temperature can be lowered, or blood pressure regulated.

Learning biofeedback is expensive, since various pieces of electronic equipment must be used. Most people interested in this approach to reducing stress enroll in a course through a local college or hospital. In this way, access to the needed equipment may be obtained at a relatively low cost.

Biofeedback is effective in making a person feel calm and relaxed. It is also effective in helping people with specific disorders such as migraine headaches, certain circulatory illnesses, and alcoholism and drug addiction. It is, however, a short-term relaxation technique. It does not remove the source of tension or anxiety from an individual's life, and therefore the stress may recur.

Benson (1975) cites a number of the drawbacks to using biofeedback. He states that it is limiting in that only one change can be accomplished at a given time. The muscles in one area of the body may be relaxed, but, although this may precipitate relaxation in other muscles, total relaxation is not ensured. Furthermore, biofeedback involves the use of expensive equipment to monitor physiological changes. Use of the required electronic devices must be obtained through courses or medical centers and usually requires the aid of a qualified psychiatrist, psychologist, or health practitioner. Attending courses and spending money may cause some degree of stress. Another problem is related to home biofeedback devices that are advertised as capable of providing needed information on physiological changes. These devices are generally ineffective and should be avoided unless recognized and approved by qualified medical personnel.

## Meditation

Meditation is a relaxation process in which a person reduces blood pressure and the need for oxygen through a calm, restful thought period. It is a brief mental escape from daily routine, and may be practiced by anyone. Transcendental meditation (TM) has become one of the more popular meditation techniques. It is a process in which an individual applies certain techniques to temporarily escape from normal, logical mental processes. The person practicing transcendental meditation seeks a quiet, calm environment and sits there in a comfortable position. He or she then attempts to separate himself or herself from all external thoughts. (To this point, TM is similar to most meditation processes.) In order to accomplish this mental separation a "mantra," or secret word, is repeated to direct the mind away from the normal, often stressful, mental processes. During TM, most people keep their eyes closed and breath in a slow, relaxed manner.

Transcendental meditation is practiced twice a day. Each period lasts for approximately 20 minutes, and they are often conducted before the morning and evening meals. Studies at the University of California and the Harvard University have shown that during any form of meditation an individual's rate of metabolism and need for oxygen are reduced. Studies also show that brain patterns indicated that the person was at rest.

Those who practice transcendental meditation state that it improves memory and learning and that it also improves emotional stability, although this has not been supported scientifically. Winter notes that TM has been shown to have both physiological and emotional benefits (Winter, 1976).

## Hypnosis

Dr. Herbert Spiegel, of the Columbia University College of Physicians and Surgeons, states that a close relationship exists between transcendental meditation, biological feedback, hypnosis, and other techniques that require an attentive, narrowed concentration to ease or erase external distractions (McQuade and Aikman, 1974). Spiegel's studies have shown that each of these methods is extremely useful in reducing stress. As one of the world's experts in scientific hypnosis, he champions this technique in reducing stress and addressing the problems that underlie it.

Theatrical hypnosis, the type used in carnivals and on television talk shows, is different from the hypnosis used in reducing stress. However, many of the perceptions people have about hypnosis have evolved from these theatrical applications. As a result, there are a number of misperceptions about its use and nature. It is not, for example, a state of unconsciousness. Instead, a person under hypnosis has an enhanced awareness of and sensitivity toward his or her surroundings. The person never loses control of his or her senses or mental or physical processes. Instead, the person loses only some conscious feeling of control. He or she is fully capable of taking control in any situation or crisis. No one can be hypnotized against his or her will. Instead, a person allows himself or herself to fall or slip into the hypnotic state.

Woolfolk and Richardson (1978) define hypnosis as "the altered state of consciousness that results from focusing awareness on a set of suggestions and allowing oneself to be receptive to those suggestions—all while allowing free reign to one's powers of imagination." Self-hypnosis is a simple technique for stress reduction that may be used by most people with a minimum of effort. Yates (1979) cites two methods of self-hypnosis: eye fixation and eye roll. The eye fixation method requires the individual to stare at a stationary object while sitting in a comfortable position. While concentrating on the object, "silently tell yourself that your eyelids are getting heavier and heavier and that pretty soon they will close and you will be very relaxed, yet fully aware. Repeat this suggestion every 60 seconds. When the eyelids are ready, let them close. Slowly take a deep breath, hold it for ten to fifteen seconds, then exhale. As you breathe comfortably, say the word 'relax' when you exhale each time" (Yates, 1979).

The eye roll method requires a person to roll his or her eyes inward and upward, trying to look at the center of the top of the forehead. The eyes should remain closed while doing so, and a deep breath should be taken, held, and released. The person opens his or her eyes and imagines that his or her body is becoming both warm and heavy. Thoughts of warmth and heaviness are directed to each of the major areas of the body. A sense of relaxation should be realized. Once this has been accomplished, a deeper trance can be obtained by taking another deep breath, holding it, and slowly exhaling while saying the word "deeper." This sequence may be repeated several times. To end this form of light trance, a person says, "I'm coming out" or "I will open my eyes when I count to 5." The person then opens his or her eyes and should feel relaxed.

Self-hypnosis simply achieves a relaxed, altered state of consciousness in which the mind can be reprogrammed. This reprogramming, which is accomplished through suggestions that an individual makes to himself or herself, is known as autosuggestion. Yates (1979) gives six basic guidelines for autosuggestion:

1. The more often a suggestion is repeated, the more effective it will be.
2. Suggestions should be stated in positive rather than negative terms.
3. Progress should be anticipated in smaller degrees of stages. Rapid and drastic changes will rarely occur in self hypnosis.
4. Physical, mental, and emotional improvements should be viewed positively, and people should realize that their chances of changing for the better are good. This concept addresses the power of positive thinking.

5. Autosuggestion should be phrased as statements rather than commands. For example, a person should not say "I must," but rather "I choose to." People resist taking orders from anyone, including themselves.
6. A person should reinforce an autosuggestion by viewing himself or herself in a positive, relaxed manner. This visual imagery is effective in making self-hypnosis work.

For self-hypnosis and autosuggestions, as for other meditation techniques, to be effective, an individual must be receptive to the technique. If he or she is skeptical or negative, the technique will not work.

## AN APPROACH TO FITNESS, HEALTH, AND STRESS REDUCTION

In *How to Kill Stress Before It Kills You*, Culligan and Sedlack (1976) describe a 13-step personal approach to coping with and reducing stress and maintaining good health. Included in their approach are the following suggestions:

1. A person should not remain in bed in the morning unless he or she is sleeping. Unless you can fall back asleep immediately after waking, you should rise and begin some activity. Even if you awaken in the middle of the night, you should participate in some activity, and then return to sleep.
2. A person should engage in exercise every morning. This is effective in maintaining good physical conditioning. It may also boost a person's morale by keeping him or her trim.
3. A shower should be taken every morning, following the exercise period. The temperature of the water should be changed from hot to cold during the shower by those who are physically fit.
4. A well-balanced breakfast should be eaten every day. Ideally, breakfast should be the largest meal of the day. Lunch should be a smaller, balanced serving of food, and dinner should be the smallest meal of the day. Most people eat a small breakfast or miss it entirely. They eat a quick, un-

balanced lunch and a large dinner. Their activity after dinner is usually slight, which has a negative effect on health. As stated earlier in this chapter, one of the most significant stressors affecting the well-being of people in the human service fields is a poor, unbalanced diet.

5. A person should engage in a light exercise routine each evening, several hours after eating or before retiring for the night.

6. People with a busy schedule should make two written lists each evening. The first list should include activities that *must* be performed the next day. The second list should include those tasks that *may* be done the next day. Most people, according to Culligan and Sedlack, find great success in completing the tasks on the first list. They also find success in completing one or two items from the second list or in eliminating some of the less important items from that list.

7. When offended, insulted, irritated, or angry, you should engage in a brief period of positive reflection. The individual should consider the source of these feelings and realize that the person who brought them on may have been wrong. However, if the person was right, the comment should be taken as a foundation for personal growth and improvement. Regardless of the source of the irritation or anger, a person should attempt to derive something positive from it rather than becoming angry.

8. People should avoid "flying off the handle." Sudden outbursts of rage rarely result in a positive outcome. A brief period of positive reflection will often assist a person in avoiding a sudden outburst of anger.

9. An individual's blood pressure should be checked regularly. A family physician will be able to advise a person on the frequency of such examinations. For those people with a family history of heart or kidney disease, such checks may be conducted monthly or quarterly.

10. Each individual should develop his or her own code of morals and ethics, replacing those that have been dictated by others but have proven inadequate. This clarification of

values will aid a person in deciding what he or she will do in any situation and will assist him or her in accepting what others do.

11. A person should take positive action toward eliminating feelings of guilt. If these feelings are the result of not having maintained contact with a friend or relative, he or she should attempt to contact that person. If he or she has guilt feelings stemming from his or her own youth or as a result of difficulties with raising his or her own children, the source of these feelings should be considered. The positive accomplishments in life should be considered, and discussions of these feelings should be shared with a trusted friend or relative. A person may call or write a friend or relative, even from the distant past. Such action will often brighten both people's days. In each case, an attempt should be made not to allow guilt feelings to interfere with a positive approach to each day's activities.

12. Each person should memorize a series of inspirational words or phrases. During periods of stress and anxiety, these words should be remembered and repeated. A person may also turn to an inspirational book or part of a book and read it silently or aloud.

13. When problems occur that are particularly stressful, an individual should take some action to address them. Such action may include exercise, relaxation, dancing, reading, eating, singing, meeting a friend, talking to family members, or crying. Laughter has also been recognized as an excellent way to reduce stress. A person may read a humorous book or watch a comedy. Laughter generally lightens the burden of daily problems and concerns. If a person spends a great deal of time thinking about the problem without taking some action to address it, the stress it creates will be compounded (Culligan and Sedlack, 1976).

## INDIVIDUAL TECHNIQUES FOR COPING

Winter (1976) notes that some of the 88 surviving crew members of the U.S.S. Pueblo, who were subjected to 11 months of con-

finement and poor treatment by the North Koreans, were able
to withstand the stress of their situation well. Others were not
able to cope with the situation. Studies of the crew members
showed that there was no significant difference in their education, social backgrounds, or religious beliefs. Those members of
the crew who coped exhibited a variety of ego defenses in follow-
up studies. These included humor, faith, rationalization, denial,
reality testing, and an ability to fantasize. Winter believes that
the average person will rarely experience the type of stress realized by the Pueblo crew. Through selecting various techniques
of coping with tension, which involves trial and error, each person will develop his or her own personal approach.

The following techniques for consideration in the development of a personal approach for coping with and reducing
stress have been adapted from Winter's recommendations.

1. A person should not allow things to drift for an extended
   period of time. The emotional and physical effects of stress
   and tension are signals that some corrective action is needed.
2. A person should attempt to identify his or her anxieties and
   fears. Once a person recognizes these elements, he or she
   can begin the process of reducing the stress they cause.
3. A person should work toward being objective in identifying
   his or her problems. Efforts should be made to avoid blam-
   ing others, although this is often a reflex action when something goes wrong. Being objective in looking at the cause of
   problems will assist a person in assuming responsibility for
   his or her own actions.
4. A person should not ignore problems; overlooking problems
   will never be a permanent solution to stress. At optimum
   times, one should attempt to confront sources of stress,
   even though this may bring temporary discomfort.
5. Doing something for others provides a person with the
   opportunity to escape the effects of his or her own stress by
   assisting other people in resolving theirs. "The ungiving
   self is the unfulfilled self" (Winter, 1976). Service to others,
   however, can be compulsive and a way of avoiding self-
   confrontation. Avoiding self-confrontation can only lead to

increasing and continuing stress. The self-sacrificial attitude of many human service professionals is an effective
guise for avoiding personal problems. In this regard, serving others compounds stress.

6. Each person should arrange to have some time alone. This
time should be free of interruptions and demands of others.
For a person working within the human service fields, where
exposure to the demands of others is a constant daily oc-
currence, this is particularly important. Privacy and time
alone may be as important to personal well-being as sleep,
exercise, and a balanced diet.

7. A person should recognize when his or her attempts at
resolving a problem are not working and should then engage in another activity. Focusing on a single problem for
too long a period may cause increased stress. Instead, a
person should become involved in other activities and return to the problem at a later, more propitious time.

8. A person should be decisive. Making a decision, whether it
be right or wrong, will cause less tension and anxiety than
indecision. A person will generally feel good when a decision is made. If it was a wrong decision, corrective action
may be taken. Indecision allows tension to persist and grow.

9. A person should seek moderation in attention to detail.
Tension is often associated with attempts to attend to every
detail no matter how minute or inconsequential. A simple
activity may be blown up out of all proportion if too much
attention is given to minute details. In fact, over-concen-
tration on details may obscure key ideas, as well as those
requiring careful attention.

10. A person should assess his or her view toward winning and
achieving. A person who places too much emphasis on
winning will experience continuous stress. Losing is often a
catalyst for learning, and a person who accepts losing well
will be better prepared to cope with stress. The stress that
accompanies an overemphasis on winning often begins in
youth when parents aggressively foster it in Little League or
school athletic competition.

11. A person should avoid playing a role, i.e., living a stereo-

type. Winter cites the "man in the gray flannel suit" and the "superefficient housewife" as two such roles. Others include the "supermother" and "super human service worker." Playing a role decreases a person's flexibility and often forces him or her to pretend throughout life.

12. A person should avoid judging himself or herself too harshly. A person should not expect more of himself or herself than do others. Attempting to maintain one's self as a flawless model for others to follow results in stress and its accompanying headaches, backaches, and ulcers.

13. A person should maintain a high level of respect for himself or herself. When a person does not, others will often accept this evaluation. When this occurs, stress mounts. A positive personal image within the community, the work environment, and the family is contingent on self-respect.

14. A person should accept and be willing to compromise. Maintaining flexibility in approaching people and situations is an effective technique for avoiding stress. Rigidity in dealing with others and with daily situations is a primary cause of tension.

15. During periods in which stress begins to build, a person should seek a change in his or her activity or environment. This may include a vacation, a one-day trip with family members, or even rearranging furniture in the home.

16. Routine activities can be a cause of stress if not balanced with change. A person should change a routine whenever it begins to cause tension. Changes in routine may include finding a new route to work, shopping at a new store, walking instead of driving to a location, having a large meal in the middle of the day, adding romantic touches and times to lovemaking, or engaging in a new form of recreation.

17. When anger begins to mount, a person should attempt to work it off immediately. This may involve taking a walk, participating in physical labor, or engaging in a sport. Physical exercise is one of the most effective ways to reduce the strain and tension that accompany feelings of anger.

18. A person should associate with people who are constructive

and supportive. Association with people who are constantly critical will cause a person to become inefficient and unhappy. His or her self-concept will be lowered. By associating with positive people, this may be avoided.

19. A person should attempt to strike a balance between work and leisure time. When either one becomes too consuming, stress grows. An individual should take a positive outlook toward finding sources of satisfaction both in the work environment and during leisure time.

20. To relax physically in times of stress, a person should take a warm bath and, if possible, get a brief massage. This relaxes the muscles and makes a person feel at ease.

There are a variety of other techniques a person may use to reduce and cope with stress and the tensions and anxiety that cause it. They include:

Setting realistic life goals
Seeking advice of friends when under stress
Focusing on present activities and not placing too much emphasis on events that occurred in the past or that will occur in the future
Improving listening skills to better understand what others are saying and to better analyze personal conversation
Seeking humor in most situations
Reading books
Listening to music
Becoming involved in community activities

## REDUCING CONSUMPTION OF COFFEE, SMOKING, DRUGS, AND ALCOHOL TO REDUCE STRESS

Numerous studies have shown conclusively that coffee and smoking induce stress, although many people turn to these items when in need of tension reduction. For example, a cup of coffee contains a minimum of 100 mg of caffeine. People who have ingested 250 mg of caffeine exhibit the same symptoms as those suffering from clinical anxiety. Smoking has a similar effect, since nicotine is a stimulant that causes a person's heart rate to begin climbing.

Yates (1979) cites the Eltra Corporation, Converse Rubber Company study on relaxation breaks. Instead of the usual coffee break, often taken in haste by employees, the company gave two experimental groups a 15-minute relaxation break twice each day for a period of 2 months. Two control groups were not given these breaks and continued to function according to their normal work pattern. At the end of the period, the experimental groups exhibited lowered blood pressure, fewer headaches, fewer problems with sleep, improved interaction with others, and improved job satisfaction.

Relaxation breaks may include quiet rest periods away from the actual work environment. They may include periods of meditation, walks outside, brief and simple exercises, or group activities with fellow workers. Some companies have begun to provide comfortable settings for relaxation breaks to balance the traditional vending machine area that offers coffee and cigarettes. The concept of relaxation breaks make use of the principle of deviation, which Selye states is of therapeutic value in coping with and reducing stress. Relaxation breaks are detailed in Chapter 6.

Those people who are habitual coffee drinkers should try alternatives. Decaffeinated coffee and herb teas are hot beverages that are less harmful, whereas cola and most commercial teas contain caffein in quantities only slightly less than coffee. Also, a cup of water or juice often satisfies a person's craving to sip a beverage while they work.

A variety of techniques and programs have been publicized in recent years to assist habitual smokers in quitting. Classes are conducted by many colleges, universities, public health agencies, the American Lung Association, the American Heart Association, and private organizations that focus on group activities. In these classes, smokers provide support to other smokers. Family physicians have helped many people give up smoking through programs designed to meet individual needs. Hypnosis has also proven effective in aiding some people in breaking their smoking habit.

Regardless of the technique used, habitual smokers and coffee drinkers should attempt to end their habits. Both activities compound the effects of stress. By reducing coffee intake and cigarette smoking, stress will be reduced and health improved.

Human service professionals also grow dependent on drugs and alcohol to escape daily stress. Some practitioners turn to them to remain awake; others use them to sleep. Some people, such as physicians, nurses, and dentists, have ready access to drugs during those periods when they feel the need for an external stimulant. Practitioners will use drugs and alcohol to expand their capabilities by allowing them to work longer and to remain calm when dealing with clients, patients, and students. Whatever the reason, these habits often lead to physical dependency. The original purpose for drinking or taking drugs then becomes secondary to this dependency.

Breaking drug and alcohol habits is difficult, and generally requires professional and family support. It also requires desire and willingness to change on the part of the affected individual. Assistance is available through local health departments, private and public hospitals and clinics, counseling services, Alcoholics Anonymous, and alcohol and drug abuse treatment centers. Most of these services are free or low in cost, and all personal information is held confidential.

## SUMMARY

How each individual responds to stress is based on a wide variety of variables, including personality, health, work environment, and family and cultural factors. The techniques and approaches for coping with and reducing stress are equally varied. For people in the human service fields, applying some of these techniques in a stress reduction program will result in improved physical and mental health and emotional stability.

A person embarking on such a program should first consider his or her needs, limitations, and capabilities. For example, someone with weak knees would not gain from jogging as a stress reduction technique. Instead, the stress would be compounded. A person who has difficulty reading would experience more stress if he or she relied upon books as an escape from stress. In each situation, a person should carefully select those stress reduction and coping techniques that can be implemented with a minimum of difficulty.

Primary techniques for coping with and reducing stress focus on physical well-being and stability in the home and work environments. Exercise has been proven to be one of the most effective of all stress reduction techniques. However, anyone engaging in an exercise program should consider the precautions listed in this chapter and should consult a physician first. Once an exercise program is begun, it should be remembered that aerobic exercises, those that force oxygen rapidly into the blood, are more effective in maintaining good health and reducing stress than are strength exercises, such as weightlifting. Brisk walking and swimming are among the best aerobic exercises.

Although the precise relationship between stress and diet is unclear, most professionals acknowledge that an interaction exists and that an improved diet has a significant effect on the way in which a person copes with tension and anxiety. About 40% of the average American's calorie intake comes from fats. The daily diet of the average human service practitioner, which consists of fast foods, excessive salt, and large amounts of coffee, is exceedingly high in fats (including cholesterol), sugar, salt, and caffeine, all of which can contribute to stress in various ways, as well as having a negative impact on health.

The primary factor in effective food intake is a balanced diet. This should include two or more servings daily from the milk and meat groups and four or more servings daily from the fruit and vegetable and bread and cereal groups.

For anyone who is overweight and interested in losing weight, a physician should be consulted before any diet is attempted. There are no simple, rapid diets that result in long-term weight loss. Any long-term weight loss requires work on the part of the individual and a modification of eating behavior. When dieting, a vitamin and mineral supplement should be taken.

Good mental health practices are as important to coping with and reducing stress as good physical health practices. The individual must aggressively approach good mental health practices and must develop a sense of commitment to them. Such practices involve maintaining a positive outlook toward others, an enthusiastic approach to work, and a realistic attitude toward goals.

Biofeedback, transcendental meditation, and hypnosis are among the techniques an individual may pursue to reduce and cope with stress. Each of these processes allows the individual to control his or her body and the physical effects of stress on it through mental or thought activity. Each process requires some study and practice. These techniques have proven effective in reducing a person's blood pressure and muscle tension.

A person can select the coping techniques that most effectively fit his or her individual needs. In all cases, an individual should experiment with techniques for coping with and reducing stress until a personal approach can be developed. This personal approach should be comfortable to the individual so that it does not cause additional stress. Utilizing the techniques outlined in this chapter requires that a person first recognize that stress is omnipresent and that he or she must make a commitment to cope with and reduce it. In addition to the techniques outlined in this and the following chapter, others may be discovered by reviewing some of the texts and documents listed in the references and the Suggested Additional Reading list and by visiting local libraries, colleges, universities, and public health services.

# Chapter 6
# Coping with and Reducing Stress Administratively

There are a wide variety of techniques available to individuals to assist them in coping with and reducing the effects of negative stress. There are an equally extensive number of techniques available to the administrators and managers of agencies and organizations to assist their employees in coping with and reducing the stress experienced as a result of their jobs. To be effective in battling the impact of stress, both the individual and the agency or organization must share responsibility.

Three basic choices are available to people and agencies in managing stress, whether they are in the human service fields, units of government, or private business and industry: (1) they may choose to develop coping mechanisms to deal with stress as it exists (i.e., they tolerate the stress situation, taking no action to remove or reduce it); (2) they may fight the effects of stress by implementing programs and techniques designed to remove or minimize the causes of stress; and (3) they may withdraw or retreat from the source of the stress (i.e., they may remove themselves from the environment in which the stress is experienced) (Yates, 1979). Each of these approaches (tolerating, fighting, and retreating) can be effective ways of responding to stress.

Many how-to books and articles have been written to assist people in coping with and reducing stress. New interest was generated in reducing stress on the job and in the home in the late 1970s. Government, business, and industry began sponsoring workshops and seminars on stress awareness and stress management. Personnel managers began specializing in employee stress reduction. Techniques to reduce stress and improve health and well-being that were unknown prior to this period, such as biofeedback and hypnotherapy, began growing in popularity. Television programs on stress management have appeared in prime-time hours on both commercial and educational networks.

## BENEFITS OF ADMINISTRATIVE AND AGENCY PROGRAMS

Increased awareness of the impact of stress has placed pressure on many agency administrators to focus attention on their work environment and the work environment of their employees. Administrators who desire to cope with and reduce stress within their agencies can pass out available literature, provide counseling to employees, and sponsor programs on stress awareness and management. The implementation of stress awareness and management activities will benefit both the agency and the employee (Yoder and Heneman, 1958). The agency will benefit through:

Increased output and improved productivity
A reduction in employee turnover and absenteeism
Increased employee morale
Increased employee loyalty
Increased participation by practitioners in agency planning activities
Reduced grievances
Improved public and community relations
An enhanced recruitment effort to draw others to the field

The benefits to individuals and practitioners who participate in agency-sponsored stress reduction and management programs include:

Increased job satisfaction
Improved relations with peers and supervisors
A reduction in the amount of stress and its effects that is carried
    over into the home environment
Reduced feelings of insecurity
Improved health
Increased enthusiasm toward job performance
Improved relations with patients, clients, students, and others

Administrators considering stress reduction and stress management programs within their agencies will generally be concerned with such factors as program cost, the ease or difficulty with which the program may be implemented, and the ultimate impact on employees. The following list represents some of the activities that may be implemented in an agency's stress management program. The agency or organization may consider implementing one, several, or all of these activities. Each of them is subsequently developed in this chapter.

Administrative education
Mid-management education
Staff and field service education
Coordination with the employees' organizations
Career development alternatives
Counseling services (personal, vocational, preretirement, and
    post-crisis)
Family orientation program
Phased retirement systems
Reassignment programs
Employee exchange programs
Vacation scheduling
Health care and physical development programs
Alcohol and drug rehabilitation programs
Professional liability insurance
Education enhancement programs

Transportation assistance
Establishing priorities and objectives
Communication
Selection and promotional practices
Programs of prevention
Miscellaneous administrative and agency programs

## Administrative Education

For stress reduction and management programs to be successful within an agency or organization, they must be fully supported by administrative personnel. The first step in gaining this support is to provide administrators with an overview of the negative effects of stress and the techniques and activities designed to address them. Educational programs for administrative personnel may range from a brief introductory course in stress awareness to a detailed seminar on developing and implementing stress management programs. Programs may be provided to an agency by private consulting firms, local universities and community colleges, and other agencies that have had experience in stress management.

A variety of learning materials are available to supplement the educational programs offered to administrative personnel. Training bulletins, texts, and brochures provide help to administrators. They can be obtained through professional associations and societies such as the American Management Association, the International Personnel Management Association, the International Association of Chiefs of Police, Blue Cross and Blue Shield organizations, and others.

Any administrative educational program or self-help guide on stress management should include information on planning, evaluation, personnel management, and counseling, since each of these areas are essential to the success of an agency's efforts. Administrative personnel must become increasingly aware that stress reduction and control are parts of the normal, daily managerial process. They should not be treated as separate and distinct program activities. If handled as separate entities, the success of the total managerial process will be diminished.

To avoid this, each of the following areas should be incorporated in a total administrative effort to manage stress. The dimensions of the total program need to be clarified in the administrative education component.

## Mid-management Education

Educating mid-management or supervisory personnel about the impact of stress and in techniques for coping with stress is as important as educating administrators. Supervisory personnel in most agencies and organizations bear responsibility for major decision-making and for the direct daily management of personnel. They are involved in counseling and in evaluating personnel and, in some cases, they dictate the daily activities of field practitioners. The atmosphere in which many work groups exist is established by first-line supervisors.

In addition to techniques for stress reduction and control, any education program for mid-management personnel should include discussion on such topics as role identification, techniques of positive reinforcement, discipline, evaluation and performance review, motivating personnel, and concepts in participative management. Effective educational programming for supervisors will ensure a coordinated and consistent approach to stress reduction and control and to personnel management in general.

The sources for assistance in providing educational programming to supervisory personnel in this area are the same as those cited in the administrative area. However, for such programs to be effective, participation by administrative personnel is vital. Through such participation and involvement, supervisors come to know and understand that the administration of the agency or organization is committed to stress management.

## Staff and Field Service Education

All personnel within an agency should participate in a stress awareness program. This program would provide employees with worthwhile information on coping with stress and would demonstrate the agency's concern for their well-being. A stress awareness program for field practitioners should include discussions in each of the following areas:

Overview of stress and its effects on the individual
Causes of stress on the job and at home
Identifying the symptoms of job stress
Agency efforts toward stress management
Personal efforts that may be taken towards stress management
Resources to assist employees in stress management

Assistance in providing staff and field service education programs may be obtained from universities, colleges, private consulting firms, and agencies and organizations that have implemented successful stress management programs. These programs may be presented in brief sessions during lunch periods or before or after the normal work day, or as detailed workshops and seminars during normal work hours. The implementation of such programs demonstrates immediately that the agency or organization is taking an interest in the well-being of its employees.

## Coordination With Employees' Organizations

Most practitioners in the human service fields belong to some sort of employee organization. This organization may be a fraternal group, a professional association, or a union. In some agencies and organizations, an adversary relationship exists between administrators and the employees' organizations, which makes coordinated efforts toward improvements within the agency difficult or impossible to achieve. Time and energy and an abundance of good will must be devoted to overcoming obstacles within the relationship.

In those agencies in which the employees' organizations and the administration function in a coordinated manner, both the organizations and the individual practitioners benefit. Coordination may simply require a regularly scheduled meeting between employee representatives and agency administrators at which areas of mutual interest are discussed. When a mechanism for the mutual exchange of thoughts, feelings, and ideas exists, a sense of unity of purpose with the agency is fostered. Coordination of efforts also facilitates communication between administration and staff in an informal manner and in informal situations and interactions. Administrative respect for the employees' groups has the ripple effect of increasing the self-respect of each employee. Improved self-respect translates readily into stress reduction and improved stress management.

## Career Development Alternatives

Career development alternatives and incentives within an agency of organization minimize the potential for job burnout by providing employees with a variety of career options. These options may provide practitioners with different responsibilities and, perhaps, increased status. Career development alternatives and incentives may range from structured programs of specialization to informal involvement in the agencies' planning processes. In many fire departments, for example, each firefighter is responsible for a particular function, such as maintaining personnel schedules or purchasing supplies, in addition to his or her general duties as a firefighter. There are other, more complex jobs available to the firefighter, such as fire equipment operator and paramedic. When such career options are available, the employee can decide which alternative he or she would like to pursue. The agency then assists the employee in gaining the skills necessary for the specialization. Both the agency and the employee can benefit. Career development alternatives and incentives are applicable to almost all human service fields and, when effectively managed, they can prevent or reduce burnout. Many career development programs involve employee participation in the planning and managerial processes. Other provide practitioners with financial awards. For example, a police officer who becomes an investigative specialist or a specialist in training and education may receive as much as 5% additional income for serving in this career step. Financial rewards may also be given on a short-term basis. A person who serves on a committee to redevelop the agency's performance evaluation system may receive a special fee or bonus. Financial incentives may also stimulate new ideas for improved production, service delivery, quality of service, and human relations.

Information on the wide variety of career development alternatives and incentives available to agencies and organzations may be found in most modern texts on personnel management. Information and assistance may also be obtained from agencies that have successfully implemented career development and incentive programs.

## Counseling Services

An agency that initiates a counseling service program will find that this not only aids in the prevention of job stress but reduces the harmful effects of stress as well. An effective counseling service program includes personal and financial counseling, vocational and career counseling, preretirement counseling, and post-crisis counseling. The administration of the agency, with input from field practitioners, should determine how the counseling program is to be implemented. Methods of maintaining privacy and confidentiality and payment guidelines should be established before any counseling program is begun.

*Personal and family counseling* should be available to practitioners on an as-needed basis. In addition, policies and procedures and the human aspects should be clearly defined so that supervisors and administrators will feel comfortable in referring an employee who exhibits the warning signs of job stress for counseling services.

*Vocational counseling* should focus on assisting employees in understanding or enhancing job skills, and on long-term career planning. Many employees are not aware of the career options available to them within their agency. Vocational counseling demonstrates agency interest in employee well-being.

*Preretirement counseling* should be included to assist employees in preparing for their retirement in advance of their final work date. This counseling should include guidance on beginning second careers and on techniques for taking full advantage of leisure time. Without effective guidance and planning, retirement can be one of the most stressful periods of life, resulting in physical and mental disfunctioning and, in some cases, in suicide.

*Post-crisis counseling* is an excellent way to cope with many of the stressors unique to the human service fields. A police officer who is forced to shoot a suspect, a firefighter who sees a colleague seriously injured, a social worker who is unable to aid a family in need, and a teacher exposed to severe disciplinary problems in the classroom are facing personal, job-related crises that can increase disillusionment, loneliness, and burnout and affect mental and physical health. Supervisors and administrators who are sensitive to such situations may encourage affected practitioners to meet with the staff counselor to prevent the incidents from having a profound effect both on the employee's current state of health and on his or her future performance.

Those agencies that cannot afford paid counseling services or whose staffs are too small to warrant paid counselors may seek out a variety of alternative strategies. Counseling programs may be established in conjunction with area hospitals, universities, and public health agencies. Local clergy are frequently educated and experienced in counseling techniques and are usually agreeable to providing their services to human service agencies. Larger organizations that employ staff counselors will often assist smaller agencies in obtaining counseling services. Because of the sensitive nature of the human service professions in dealing with the lives of others, exposure to the stress caused by crises is great. Effective counseling services are vital to preventing and reducing the long-term negative effects of job stress.

## Family Orientation Program

To aid in reducing family stress, a family orientation program may be established. In this program, husbands, wives, children, parents, and others who have a close relationship to the human service practitioner are given an overview of the agency's or-organization's daily activities. They gain an understanding of the work that is performed, how this work affects clients, and why it often creates a stressful environment for the practitioner.

Relatives and friends of the practitioner may be invited to tour facilities and view any equipment used by the practitioner. They may also be provided with a summary of the benefits provided to employees and how they may obtain detailed information on them. A program on stress reduction techniques and how they may be applied within the home should be included in the program.

Family orientation programs should include several sessions each year. In this way, there is on-going interaction between family members and the human service agency. New programs, changes in agency activities or policies, and problems being experienced by the agency may be factually presented to those who attend the orientation program. Greater understanding of the role and activities of the practitioner will develop and this will ultimately serve to reduce some of the stress created in the practitioner's home by his or her human service function.

## Phased Retirement Systems

One of the most significant stressors in a person's career is retirement. For many, retirement represents positive stress, i.e., the challenge of starting a second career or of taking advantage of leisure time. For others, retirement represents negative stress, particularly if they are unprepared to cope with and take full advantage of their time. The suddenness of going from full-time employment to full-time leisure can be especially traumatic.

A phased retirement program allows a person to prepare for retirement gradually over a period of months or years. A person entering his or her last year of work before retirement, for example, may begin working only 4 days a week. At 6 months before retirement this may be reduced to only 3 days a week or to 5 days a week at half time. This phasing-out program is supplemented by retirement counseling, educational incentives, and other activities designed to assist the employee in continuing to live a productive life after retirement. Through such programming the negative stressors that often accompany retirement may be significantly reduced. Information on pre-retirement and phased retirement programs may be readily obtained from many large corporations and industries. Information on these programs is also available in most modern texts on personnel management and administration.

## Reassignment Programs

It is not uncommon for a person who has been accustomed to a single function for a long period of time to experience negative stress. The individual may be devoted to his or her function but, for reasons not in his or her control, may be experiencing job burnout. Generally, human service agencies cannot afford sabbatical programs like those offered by many colleges, universities, and educational systems, in which instructors are granted leave from their daily function at full or half salary to conduct research, to study, or to write.

*Sabbatical-type programs,* however, can be beneficial in all human service agencies. Practitioners who have been on the job for 4, 5, or 6 years may be reassigned to another function for a period of months to assist with an administrative project or to conduct a special program within the agency. On completion of the project they are returned to their regular function. In this way they will gain leave from the regular activity, gain an understanding of another function within their agency, and often gain new skills to enhance the quality of their performance. When sabbatical-type positions are created, advertisements for the positions should be prominently displayed and communicated to *all* eligible employees.

## Employee Exchange Programs

Directly paralleling reassignment programs are employee exchange programs, which may reduce job stress and burnout in the human service professions. This effort requires that two agencies performing similar functions exchange employees for a designated period of time. Practitioners who participate in the program are thus exposed to the problems and concerns of other human service agencies. They also gain a practical knowledge of the techniques used by other agencies to provide service to clients, students, or patients.

Social welfare agencies, educational systems, police departments, fire departments, and hospitals find that this program enhances the attitude and performance of both the practitioners who participate in the exchange and the employees who remain within the organization. There is a novelty and drama to interacting with new people that serves as an incentive to improved performance by all those affected. New skills are learned and existing skills are enhanced through interaction with people who have different work experiences. An exchange may range from several days to many months, depending on the agency's desired outcome. Exchange programs have worked successfully in private industry, the military, and in many European human service agencies for many years.

## Vacation Scheduling

Many human service practitioners experience stress in scheduling their vacations. They hesitate to take vacations because they feel a sense of obligation to providing continuous service to clients. This is particularly true for such practitioners as social workers and public health nurses, who most regularly deal with personal and family crises. Stress related to vacation scheduling may be reduced by assuring practitioners that adequate follow-up care will be provided to clients and that follow-up support will be given to special projects. The agency must devote planning time and financial and human resources to ensuring continuation of services and projects.

Whenever possible, agency administrators should encourage practitioners to plan their vacations. Discussions should be held with supervisory personnel regarding the employee's plans. This type of informal vacation planning will prevent practitioners from missing vacations or taking sporadic 1- or 2-day vacations simply to utilize accumulated leave. Vacations are intended to provide employees with an escape from the strain and monotony of the work environment and to provide them with renewed energy for the work year ahead.

## Health Care and Physical Development Programs

Because of the significant effect of stress on physical well-being, few programs will have as much impact as those designed to improve and maintain the health of employees. Health care programs within a human service agency may range from simply providing literature to employees to a large-scale program that includes medical examinations. Each agency will have to determine the extent to which it can implement health care and physical development programs. Some agencies, such as hospitals and clinics, have ready access to physicians to give assistance in establishing these programs. Other agencies may have to obtain assistance through local health departments and other sources.

Health care programs should include medical screening or medical examinations. If the cost of medical examinations is prohibitive, screening programs that provide a series of simple tests may be established with the aid of local nursing schools, public health nurses, or health departments. These programs may include such tests as tuberculosis screening, simple hearing and vision screening, blood pressure screening, a height and weight comparison, urinalysis and venereal disease screening, and pap tests. Wherever possible, blood sample analysis for diseases should also be included. Most of these tests are available through local and state agencies, and with proper planning may be easily provided to human service agencies.

Medical records on all practitioners should be maintained. These records should include information on medical history and any relevant data to illnesses, injury, and sick leave. The records should be reviewed regularly by administrators in conjunction with a physician or public health nurse. This review will enable the administrators to identify trends that may indicate that an employee is exhibiting physical effects of stress.

Once a medical screening or examination program has been established, the agency should implement health care and physical development programs. This may include information and short courses on nutrition, weight control programs, and activities designed to promote regular exercise. Assistance in implementing these programs may be obtained from local health departments, hospitals, and colleges and universities. Exercise is one of the best techniques for reducing stress, and employees should be encouraged to participate in a regularly scheduled physical development program (see Chapter 5).

## Alcohol and Drug Rehabilitation Programs

It is not uncommon for people to turn to alcohol and drugs to escape job stress. Abuse of these substances is particularly common in the human service fields, in which practitioners are exposed to human grief on a regular basis. Many agencies fail to recognize alcoholism and drug abuse because the symptoms are not highly visible. A physician, a teacher, or a police officer may take pills to remain calm or alert. The effects of the drug may actually heighten performance on a temporary or short-term basis, thus masking the problem. Generally, it is only when the problem becomes profound and interferes with performance that it is recognized by supervisors and administrative personnel. Sadly, when the illness becomes severe, it is often the lack of performance on the part of the individual practitioner that gains the attention of supervisors and administrators and not the underlying pathology. The illness is not addressed; instead, the employee receives a poor evaluation, is disciplined, or is fired. Therefore, the first step toward the implementation of any drug and alcohol abuse program must be the education of administrative and supervisory personnel so that they are more sophisticated observers and can react more sensitively.

Assistance in establishing alcohol and drug rehabilitation programs may be obtained from local health departments and private organizations that give full attention to implementing such programs.

## Professional Liability Insurance

Most agencies maintain liability insurance on each practitioner. In the event a mistake or error in judgment is made that may lead to legal action, both the agency and the employee are protected. Those agencies that do not maintain professional liability insurance should obtain it. Those agencies that do have professional liability insurance should make their members aware of this important fringe benefit. The existence of liability coverage is likely to reduce anxiety in the work environment and to reduce stress by creating a greater sense of freedom and discretion in decision making.

## Education Enhancement Programs

Few activities enhance the quality of job performance as much as on-going in-service educational programs that truly meet employee interests and needs. As existing skills are enhanced and new skills are learned, practitioners gain renewed enthusiasm toward their assigned functions. Participation in stimulating in-service educational programs also provides temporary relief from routine daily activities.

In-service educational programs must be relevant, well-planned, and taught by qualified professionals. Programs that are boring, irrelevant, and/or poorly presented may cause negative stress. Programs of poor quality do little to enhance employee skills.

In-service educational programs may be either optional or required. They may be offered during the work day or before or after normal work hours. Programs may also be short-term, ranging from 15-minute sessions to half-day seminars, or they may be long-term, requiring several days or weeks. Time allotments and constraints depend on the subject matter and on the needs of the agency.

The natural tendency is to seek help from outside consultants. However, many agencies and organizations will find that the expertise needed to provide effective in-service educational programs exists among their own employees. A practitioner who is called on to provide an in-service educational program generally feels that he or she has been recognized by the administration as having achieved a certain standard of excellence in a specific area. Teaching an in-service program becomes an incentive to the designated instructor. When instructors cannot be found among an agency's personnel, assistance may be obtained from local colleges and universities or from other agencies that have personnel who possess the desired skills and knowledge.

Assisting employees in furthering their own education is another way in which to reduce the effects of job stress. Tuition reimbursement programs and arrangements with local colleges to allow agency employees to participate in courses are two ways in which an educational program may be implemented. A practitioner who decides to return to college through the agency program may experience the stress that often accompanies higher education. The nature of the stress experienced in learning, however, is invariably healthy and allows a practitioner to physically and emotionally escape from the stress experienced on the job. In most cases, participation by employees in an agency-sponsored higher education program will benefit both the agency and the individual practitioner.

Similar benefits may be derived by agencies that offer informal programs of learning. These programs may be unrelated to the functions of the agency and may be offered either before or after normal working hours. Such educational enrichment and diversion programs may include aerobic dancing, local history, effective writing, speed reading, gourmet cooking, and other recreational and personal growth subjects. Most local community colleges are equipped to provide assistance in implementing such activities, and many can be implemented on-site in agency offices during lunch periods and before and after normal work hours.

## Transportation Assistance

In many of the human service fields, practitioners are required to spend great lengths of time in travel from one place to another. They travel to conferences, workshops, retreats, conventions, and client residences. In many agencies budget constraints prevent practitioners from being provided with vehicles, and they generally use their own. Whenever possible, an agency should reimburse practitioners for expenses incurred for transportation through an established travel reimbursement program. The sum allotted for travel, whether it be on a per-mile or per-day basis, should be equitable and should include the cost of fuel and vehicle maintenance and related expenses. Such programs benefit both the agency and practitioners by preventing the employee from feeling that excessive demands are being made and promoting an atmosphere of concern on the part of the employer.

## Establishing Priorities and Objectives

Employees work most effectively when they have a clear understanding of the tasks they are to perform and the expectations placed on them. This is true in the human service fields, government service, business, and industry. An employee who does not have an understanding of his or her assigned tasks and who must establish his or her own priorities will experience a high degree of job stress.

In establishing priorities for a individual practitioner, an agency must first articulate its missions or goals. Once the broad goals of the agency are established, specific priorities may be dictated to personnel. This may be accomplished through formal processes such as management by objectives or may be achieved through an informal memorandum establishing priorities for employees and creating the parameters within which they will function and by which they will be evaluated. A social worker, for example, must know whether the agency expects him or her to spend the majority of the work day making personal contacts rather than preparing written reports. A police officer needs to be told that the department puts greater emphasis on neighborhood crime prevention than on traffic enforcement activities. If this is not done, the social worker or police officer is likely to function in a random manner and will experience stress as he or she attempts to accomplish too many tasks within a given work period. Similarly, a school administrator must inform a classroom teacher of the educational objectives of the school and the community. Without these objectives, the teacher may spend too much time on a particular subject area in which he or she has personal interest and skills at the expense of other subjects.

When goals, priorities, and objectives are clearly defined and made known to practitioners, the entire agency functions toward a similar end. Coordination among practitioners is enhanced, tasks are understood, and job stress is reduced.

## Communication

Communication among practitioners, supervisors, and administrators has a significant impact on employee morale and job stress. Studies have suggested that improved communication within an agency or organization has resulted in higher levels of morale (Yoder and Heneman, 1958). Other purposes of communications are to:

Promote employee loyalty, cooperation, and understanding
Inform management of the needs of practitioners
Inform administrators of how practitioners respond to established priorities, objectives, policies, and agency practices
Inform, explain, and interpret to practitioners the various agency programs and special projects and the rationale behind them
Obtain and promote group teamwork
Promote personal contacts and enhance employee involvement in managerial processes
Provide means of expression and clarification
Gain an understanding of and respond to the personal and job needs of practitioners
Motivate practitioners

When the administrators within an agency communicate effectively with practitioners, an exchange of ideas generally occurs. If the communication is effective, both the agency and the practitioners benefit. To achieve this end, regular communication should occur between administrators and field practitioners. This may be accomplished through regularly scheduled meetings, information meetings, newsletters, and memoranda. These vehicles of communication should be made available on a regularly scheduled basis and should include information that is clear, concise, and accurate.

Job stress is reduced when communication is candid and when attention is given to timing. Willis notes that candor and timing are generally more important than the format of the communication (Yoder and Heneman, 1958).

## Selection and Promotional Practices

Ambiguous, unfair, and arbitrary selection and promotional processes will generally cause a high degree of job stress in employees. Hiring and promoting people who are not prepared to adequately perform assigned tasks is destructive to employee morale. Promotional and selection processes that allow for favoritism and "politics" often result in high level of employee attrition. An individual's potential, skills, and abilities are rarely considered when personal biases enter the promotional and selection processes.

Selection and promotional processes may vary from agency to agency depending on such characteristics as size, governmental provisions and restrictions, geographic locations, budget, and labor contracts. These processes may include preliminary screening, review of written examinations, reference checks, performance appraisals, psychological testing, physical examinations, and interviews.

Each agency or organization should review its selection and promotional processes annually to ensure that they meet existing needs. Emphasis should be placed on obtaining the most competent candidates for both entry-level and supervisory positions. When the selection and promotional processes are equitable, job stress within the organization is reduced, and the individual employees as well as the agency benefit.

Assistance in reviewing and establishing effective selection and promotional processes can be obtained from private consultants, local businesses and industries, and other agencies that have successfully implemented sound programs. Model programs have been based on forced-choice evaluation systems and management by objectives. Texts such as Yoder and Heneman's *Handbook of Personnel Management and Labor Relations* (1958) are excellent guides.

## Programs of Prevention

Many of the human service fields respond to the needs of people only after an incident has occurred. A police officer is called when a crime has taken place; a physician is called when someone has become ill; a social worker responds when a family is in need of assistance; and a special educational teacher is called on after a student has failed to perform satisfactorily in school. In each of these fields, practitioners seldom experience a reduction in the need for their services. Stress is experienced in knowing that they are in a "catch-up" work situation in which the problems they are attempting to resolve increase more rapidly than do the services available to address them.

One technique for reducing this type of job stress is to have practitioners participate in programs of prevention. This approach promises to provide practitioners with a feeling of accomplishment in lessening the demand for their services. Firefighters, for example, spend a significant portion of their time surveying buildings and educating the public to ensure that fire prevention techniques are applied.

Valletutti and Christoplos (1979), referring to a multidisciplinary approach to preventing mental and physical disabilities, stated:

> Prevention requires not only an unaccustomed amount of attention to anticipated problems but an uncommon amount of interdisciplinary and interprofessional planning and programming as well. Political, industrial, agricultural, and environmental management and conservation forces, advertising agencies, and the public media, along with other widely disparate professions and interest groups, often with conflicting interests and perspectives, must all become intimately involved in cooperative efforts. At each step of the prevention process these multivariate groups must contribute their special knowledge, insights, and vision toward identifying social, environmental, health, economic, technical, and attitudinal trends; toward analyzing and predicting the wide and long-range effects of these trends as well as those

of present policies; toward planning policies to control future events; toward implementing formative and summative evaluation procedures; toward establishing monitoring systems and regulatory mechanisms; toward disseminating information to relevant implementers and consumers; and toward arousing public support of and commitment to prevention policies and practices.

The establishment of prevention systems involves four difficult procedures that require continuous interdisciplinary analysis and evaluation:

1. Objective clarification: What are the specific objectives of each of the cooperating agencies and individuals and how do these objectives complement or conflict with one another?
2. Priority identification: Which of the objectives should be given priority and why?
3. Anticipation of the effects of given conditions, situations, or environmental and human manipulations, including the impact of technology and social evolution: What has been learned by each of the agencies and individuals about types and degrees of health and safety problems that are likely to emerge during years to come as a consequence of social trends and policies? What are additional problems that are likely to emerge during individual treatment procedures?
4. Program planning and implementation: How will professionals implement efforts to (a) prevent disease or disability resulting from general social policies and (b) prevent additional problems from arising for the person afflicted with disease or disability and her/his family on a single case basis?

Prevention, as a widespread social policy adhered to by government, industry, and the general public, demands a blend of foresight and responsibility for future events—a blend that is particularly difficult in any society whose citizens are conditioned to enjoy *now* whatever pleasures and profits they can.

When effective prevention programs are implemented, practitioners become more enthusiastic toward their assigned tasks. For example, a police officer who is provided with skills so that he or she can inform a resident of how to secure a home against burglary may feel a sense of accomplishment in having possibly prevented a felony. Similarly, a school administrator or teacher who can convince the parents of a hearing-impaired child to enroll their son or daughter in a rehabilitation program may gain satisfaction in knowing that he or she may have prevented that child from entering school at a disadvantage.

Prevention programs are being implemented in many of the human service fields. These programs include educating practitioners in prevention techniques and utilization of mass media to increase public awareness. Prevention programs benefit the individual practitioner, the agency he or she serves, and the public.

## Miscellaneous Administrative and Agency Programs

There are many other programs that can be implemented within an agency or organization that will aid in reducing job stress. Sick leave provisions, life insurance, health insurance, and credit unions are just a few of the benefit programs that improve the work environment for the individual practitioner and, subsequently, reduce tension and strain. Such programs, however, require funding. When the funds needed to implement such programs are not available, the agency may implement a benefit package in which the employees share the cost. The benefits may be optional, allowing the individual employee to pick those that appeal to him or her most.

## EMPLOYEE INPUT

When implementing programs to benefit employees and reduce job stress, agency administrators must obtain input from individual practitioners. Involving field practitioners in planning stress reduction activities of the agency will, in itself, aid in reducing stress. When programs are implemented without employee input, they often create additional stress because they may be irrelevant to the needs of workers.

# Chapter 7
# Implications
# and Considerations

Declining fiscal resources and an increasingly high turnover rate among burned-out practitioners are causing many administrators and planners in the human service fields to seek alternatives to traditional approaches to delivering service to clients, students, and patients. Compounding these problems are those arising from the accountability movement. Program evaluation and accountability bring increased professional and community scrutiny, with special attention directed to cost effectiveness.

For human service practitioners, attempting to provide service to people in an age of increased fiscal and programmatic constraint has escalated the stress that accompanies the responsibility they have for the well-being of others. As a result, many practitioners are seeking new employment in areas in which they experience less stress and receive higher wages and better benefits. Private business and industry are attracting many of them.

In private business and industry, increased recognition has been given to stress reduction and management programs. In-service training programs for employees, medical screening and physical development programs, relaxation breaks, vacation scheduling based on seniority, and phased retirement programs are just a few of the stress reduction activities employed by many major corporations. Reducing job stress is one technique for increasing the effectiveness and efficiency of employees, which invariably translates into increased profits for the business enterprise.

In addition, many businesses and industries have recognized the value of psychological screening as a pre-employment practice. This has been particularly effective in selecting personnel to function in high-pressure jobs. Some companies utilize prepared screening devices such as the California Psychological Inventory in addition to psychological interviews. Others use specially designed screening programs, developed to meet specific needs. Such screening, which has been used only minimally in the human service fields, has proven effective in selecting employees who have a lower frequency of illness, increased productivity, and increased longevity on the job.

Pre-employment screening processes have particularly significant implications for the human service fields. Traditionally, most organizations and agencies have relied on an individual's educational and employment credentials as criteria for selection. In some professions, an internship period may have been required in addition to formal education. Few of the human service fields have attempted to measure a job candidate's potential for coping with stress. Yet, such screening would be effective in the selection of, for example, social workers, teachers, nurses, and police officers. Tests of this kind would also be effective in selecting personnel for promotions and for assignment to specialty functions within the agency or organization.

## TEAM APPROACH TO BUILDING THE PROGRAM

Each individual must assume responsibility for his or her own well-being and for coping with and reducing stress. The administration of an agency or organization and the officers of a professional association also have an obligation to aid practitioners in coping with and reducing job stress. The most effective approach to fulfilling these obligations is one in which first-line practitioners and administrators function as a team in addressing job stress. Both groups will benefit from their efforts as part of a stress management team.

The first function of the stress management team should be the identification of specific and significant stressors affecting employees and the agency as a whole. Administrators and field practitioners will each have their own perspective as to the sources of stress and how they may be addressed. Once the stressors are identified, the scientific method should be applied in dealing with them. This involves careful identification of the specific problem to be addressed, analysis of the alternatives available to resolve it, application of the best available alternative, and evaluation of the results. In applying this method of dealing with stress, the alternatives available to address its cause should be explored. Once alternatives have been developed, a realistic, cost-effective plan of implementation should be developed.

The stress management team may consist of several administrators, mid-managers, and field or first-line practitioners. For physicians, dentists, psychologists, and others who belong to professional associations, the stress management team may consist of several association staff members and several practicing association members. In all cases, the stress reduction and management program should be implemented only after all levels of personnel within the profession have had input into the development of the process. This aids in eliminating much of the "us versus them" attitude that often destroys effective programs when they have been developed by only one constituency in an agency or organization.

In addition to allowing for input from several levels of personnel, the stress management team approach may result in the development of new techniques for coping with and reducing job stress as well as the enhancement of proven ones. It will provide for the effective identification of stressors, often before they cause serious concern. In this regard, the team becomes a catalyst for the prevention of stress. The communication that will occur between managers and field practitioners will also result in a reduction of stress as each group recognizes that it is playing a role in the well-being of the other.

## CONSIDERATIONS IN IMPLEMENTATION

In implementing a stress reduction and management program, sufficient time should be allotted for "selling." Overnight acceptance of a stress reduction program by human service practitioners is rare. They have bought the image of being tireless, dedicated, enthusiastic, and selfless. It is difficult for most of these professionals to admit that they are succumbing to the negative effects of stress as a result of their job. To overcome this barrier, an individual must first acknowledge that these negative effects of stress exist, are harmful to his or her well-being, and can be reduced. This recognition is vital to both the individual who is embarking on a personal stress reduction program and a worker who is participating in an agency-sponsored activity.

A stress management and reduction program should be implemented in phases. The professional should not attempt to diet, exercise vigorously, change work environments, and learn biofeedback in the same week. Neither should the agency or organization require medical examinations, change vacation scheduling procedures, and modify its evaluation system within the same period of time. When this occurs, the stress reduction program actually creates more stress than it reduces. Whether personal or agency sponsored, a stress reduction program should be implemented according to a specific plan with a reasonable timetable.

In implementing a plan, the practitioner or agency should include an evaluation component. In most cases, as people realize the positive effects of a stress reduction program, they will be motivated toward additional activities and toward sustaining their on-going efforts. When and how an evaluation of the program is conducted is based on the nature of the program. For example, there would be little benefit to evaluating a weight loss/nutrition program after only 1 or 2 days, or the effects of a new vacation scheduling program after only several months. If the evaluation shows weaknesses in the program, other alternatives may be explored or modifications made. The most effective stress management programs are those that have resulted from trial and error processes involving many of the stress reduction and control techniques outlined in this and allied texts.

## IMPLICATIONS FOR BUSINESS AND INDUSTRY

The implications of a stress management program for business and industry parallel those for the human service fields. The team approach to stress management will result in improved management-labor relations as a result of the communication process and the group approach toward addressing a mutual concern. Potential problems may be avoided as workers and managers discuss stresses on the job. Of significance to the private sector is the cost effectiveness of most stress management programs. Many of the programs require modifying existing procedures, conducting classes, and providing literature to employees. In most cases, however, these processes do not require excessive expenditures.

Difficulties in business and industry will be experienced, particularly if the relationship between labor and management is not good. However, working together toward the development and implementation of stress management programs may improve this interaction. In all cases, the employees initially involved in the stress management team should be volunteers.

Private consulting firms, chambers of commerce, and professional and trade associations can serve as excellent resources in the development and implementation of programs for employees. Several texts have been written on managerial approaches to dealing with stress; most are available in public libraries. The success of any stress management program, whether it be in private industry or in the human service fields, will be contingent on proper planning, involvement of all levels of the work group, and a logically formulated evaluation model.

## IMPROVED SERVICE TO PEOPLE

In addition to the benefits that the individual may derive from stress management programs and those that may be gained by his or her agency, the clients, students, and patients being served will gain. When stress levels are lowered and sources of stress are eliminated or reduced, employee attitude improves and enthusiasm increases. Response to the daily problems and concerns of others is enhanced as practitioners improve their ability to cope with the stressors that accompany them.

For the human service practitioner who is able to cope with stress, daily goal setting becomes a positive process. When stress is not addressed, the day-to-day tasks often appear overwhelming, creating added tension and anxiety. An individual who knows his or her limitations and has a realistic approach toward his or her capabilities will be an effective daily planner. He or she will therefore better meet the professional commitment to clients, patients, and students that is central to the human service professions.

# References

Anastasi, A. 1964. Fields of Applied Psychology. McGraw-Hill Book Company, New York.

Anderson, L., and Van Dyke, L. 1972. Secondary School Administration. Houghton Mifflin Company, New York.

Anderson, R. A. 1978. Stress Power: How to Turn Tension Into Energy. Human Services Press, New York.

Benson, H. 1975. The Relaxation Response. William Morrow and Company, New York.

Blythe, P. 1973. Stress Disease: The Growing Plague. St. Martin's Press, New York.

Budzynski, T. H., and Stoyva, J. 1971. Biofeedback techniques in behavior therapy and autogenic training. Unpublished manuscript.

Culligan, M., and Sedlack, K. 1976. How To Kill Stress Before It Kills You. Gosset and Dunlap Publishers, New York.

DeRosis, H. 1979. Women and Anxiety. Delacorte Press, New York.

Galton, L. 1979. The Complete Medical, Fitness, And Health Guide for Men. Simon and Schuster, New York.

Graham-Bonnalie, F. E. 1972. The Doctor's Guide to Living With Stress. Drake Publishers, New York.

Hilgard, E. R. 1953. Introduction To Psychology. Harcourt, Brace and Company, New York.

Holmes T. H., and Rahe, R. H. 1967. The social readjustment rating scale. J. Psychosomat. Res. 11:213–218.

I.A.C.P. Coping With Stress: Training Key 257. Bureau of Operations and Research, International Association of Chiefs of Police, Gaithersburg, Md.

Jahoda, M. 1979. In Grob, G. N. (ed.) Current Concepts in Positive Mental Health, Arno Press, New York.

Katch, F., McArdle, W., and Boylan, B. 1979. Getting In Shape. Houghton Mifflin Company, Boston.

Kinzer, N. S. 1979. Stress And The American Woman. Anchor Press/Doubleday, New York.

Kroes, W., Margolis B., and Hurrell, J. 1974. Job stress in policemen. J. Police Sci. Admin. 2:2.

LaMott, K. 1974. Escape From Stress. G. P. Putnam's Sons, Publishers, New York.

Levinson, H. 1970. Executive Stress. Harper and Row, New York.

McNerney, W. J. 1974. Learning to live successfully in today's world. In: Stress: Blueprint For Health. Blue Cross Association, Chicago.

McQuade, W., and Aikman, A. 1974. Stress. E. P. Dutton and Company, New York.

Mercer, J. L., and Koester, E. H. 1978. Public Management Systems. AMACOM, New York.

Pembrook, L. 1978. How To Beat Fatigue. Doubleday and Company, New York.

Phelps, L. 1977. Police Tasks And Related Stress Factors: From An Organizational Perspective. University of Nevada Press.

Selye, H. 1976. The Stress Of Life. McGraw-Hill Book Company, New York.

Tressider, J. 1977. Feel Younger, Live Longer. Rand-McNally, Chicago.

Valletutti, P., and Christoplos, F. 1979. Preventing Physical And Mental Disabilities: A Multidisciplinary Approach. University Park Press, Baltimore.

Wilson, O. 1977. Police Administration. McGraw-Hill Book Company, New York.

Winter, R. 1976. Triumph Over Tension. Grossett and Dunlap, New York.

Woolfolk, K., and Richardson, F. 1978. Stress, Sanity, and Survival. Monarch Publishers, New York.

Yates, J. E. 1979. Managing Stress. AMACOM, New York.

Yoder, D., and Heneman, H. G. 1958. Handbook Of Personnel Management and Labor Relations. McGraw-Hill Book Company, New York.

Youngdahl, B. E. 1966. Social Action and Social Work. Association Press, New York.

# Suggested
# Additional Reading

Basowitz, H., Perskey, H., Horchin, S., and Grinker, R. 1954. Anxiety and Stress. McGraw-Hill Book Company, New York.

Kraus, H. 1965. Backache, Stress and Tension: Their Cause, Prevention and Treatment. Simon and Schuster, Inc., New York.

Lazarus, R. S. 1966. Psychological Stress and the Coping Process. McGraw-Hill Book Company, New York.

McGrath, J. E. 1970. Social and Psychological Factors in Stress. Holt, Rinehart and Winston, Inc., New York.

Page, R. C. 1966. How to Lick Executive Stress. Simon and Schuster, Inc., New York.

Pelletier, K. R. 1977. Mind as Healer, Mind as Slayer. Delta Books, New York.

Selye, H. 1969. Stress without Distress. McGraw-Hill Book Company, New York.

Shaffer, L. F., and Schoben, E. J. 1956. The Psychology of Adjustment. Houghton Mifflin Company, Boston.

Tanner, O., et al. 1976. Stress. Time-Life Books, Alexandria, Va.

Toffler, A. 1970. Future Shock. Bantam Books, New York.

Welford, A. T. 1974. Man under Stress. John Wiley and Sons, Inc., New York.

Yates, J. E. 1978. Your Own Worst Enemy. Stephen Bosustow Productions, Santa Monica, Cal.

# Index

Accountability, as stressor in field service, 40–41
Adaptability, as factor in response to stress, 62
Administration
  role in stress reduction, 107–128
    approaches to, 107
    benefits of, 108–109
    education of personnel for, 110–111
    stress in, 15–17
Administrative stressors, 37–46
  accountability for decisions, 40–41
  bureaucratic procedures, 39
  performance evaluation, 42–44
  physical resource availability, 46
  policies and procedures, 38
  promotion process, 44–45
  public opinion and complaint, 42
  relations with supervisor, 39–40, 41, 43
  responsibility commensurate with authority, 45–46
  rumor (organizational), 44
  transfers, 41–42
  work schedules, 38
Aerobics, in stress reduction, 80–81

Alcohol, relation to stress, 103
Alcohol rehabilitation program, role in stress reduction, 120
Anger, displacement of, in reaction to stress, 68–69
Authority
  limited, as stressor in field service, 35
  relation to responsibility, as stressor in field service, 45–46

Biofeedback, as stress reduction technique, 90–92
Boredom, and stress, 11, 35
Bureaucratic procedures, as stressors in field service, 39
Burnout, as stressor in field service, 35–36
Business and industry, implications of stress reduction programs for, 133–134

Career development, alternatives for, role in stress reduction, 113–114
Children, stress in, 12

139